Miller
Linear Differential Equations

LINEAR DIFFERENTIAL EQUATIONS

IN THE REAL DOMAIN

LINEAR DIFFERENTIAL EQUATIONS

IN THE REAL DOMAIN

KENNETH S. MILLER *Professor of Mathematics, New York University, and Visiting Professor of Engineering Mathematics, Columbia University, 1962-64*

NEW YORK

W · W · NORTON & COMPANY · INC ·

FIRST EDITION

Library of Congress Catalog Card No. 63-8034

Published simultaneously in the Dominion of
Canada by George J. McLeod Limited, Toronto

PRINTED IN THE UNITED STATES OF AMERICA

CONTENTS

PREFACE

In this book we present certain portions of the classical and modern theory of linear differential equations in the real domain. The material not only is of interest to the pure mathematician, but contains much of the theory of ordinary differential equations used by the applied scientist. A knowledge of advanced calculus through uniform convergence and a rudimentary acquaintance with matrix theory should be sufficient prerequisite.

The basic existence and uniqueness theory along with the more elementary properties of the Wronskian forms the content of Chapter 1. The adjoint operator is introduced early (Chapter 2) since it is an indispensable tool in analyzing linear differential equations. The Green's functions for both one- and two-point boundary value problems are treated in Chapters 3 and 6 respectively. The algebra of differential operators, including a discussion of inverse operators, appears in Chapter 4. Chapter 5 on distribution theory allows us to examine certain questions concerning the solution of linear differential equations whose coefficients are not sufficiently smooth. Sturm-Liouville theory through the proof of closure and completeness is developed in Chapter 7. The class of linear differential equations with constant coefficients is disposed of in Chapter 8. We also include a proof of the Jordan theorem for matrices. Finally, in Chapter 9 we give a detailed mathematical treatment of the Frobenius method for second order linear differential equations of the Fuchs type.

Equations are numbered by sections. In Section x of Chapter A we refer to equation α simply as (α). In Section x of Chapter A we refer to equation β of Section y of Chapter A (with $x \neq y$) as ($y.\beta$). In Section x of Chapter A we refer to equation γ of Section z of Chapter B (with $A \neq B$) as ($B.z.\gamma$).

April, 1963 K.S.M.

LINEAR DIFFERENTIAL EQUATIONS

IN THE REAL DOMAIN

1

FUNDAMENTAL PROPERTIES

1. Introduction

In this book we shall be concerned mainly with *linear differential operators* such as

$$\mathbf{L} = p_0(x)\frac{d^n}{dx^n} + p_1(x)\frac{d^{n-1}}{dx^{n-1}} + \cdots + p_n(x)\cdot \tag{1}$$

and the corresponding *linear differential equation*

$$\mathbf{L}y = r(x). \tag{2}$$

More explicitly, (2) may be written as

$$p_0(x)\,y^{(n)} + p_1(x)\,y^{(n-1)} + \cdots + p_n(x)\,y = r(x). \tag{3}$$

In association with (2) we shall also introduce various initial or boundary conditions as the need arises.

Something, of course, must be said about the coefficients $p_i(x)$, $0 \leqq i \leqq n$, of $\mathbf{L}$. For the most part we shall assume that they are continuous on some closed finite interval $I = [a,b]$ of the x axis. We shall indicate this by writing† $p_i(x) \in C^0(I)$, $0 \leqq i \leqq n$. When there

† If A is any set and ξ is an element of A we express this fact by writing $\xi \in A$. This is read: "ξ is an element of A." We also use the notation $\eta \notin A$ to indicate that η is *not* an element of A.

is no necessity to indicate the interval I explicitly, or when the interval under consideration is understood, we shall simply write $p_i(x) \in C^0$, $0 \leqq i \leqq n$. We shall also recursively define $C^k(I)$, $k \geqq 1$, as the class of all functions $f(x) \in C^0(I)$ with the property that df/dx exists and belongs to $C^{k-1}(I)$. Thus $f(x) \in C^p(I)$ implies that $f(x)$ and its first p derivatives exist and are continuous on the interval I.

If $r(x) \equiv 0$ in (2), then we call $\mathbf{L}y = 0$ a *homogeneous equation*. In the contrary case we call $\mathbf{L}y = r(x)$ a *non-homogeneous equation*. The function $r(x)$ will generally be assumed to be continuous on the interval under consideration.

The adjective *linear* used in describing $\mathbf{L}$ or $\mathbf{L}y$ of course refers to the fact that

$$\mathbf{L}[\alpha f(x) + \beta g(x)] = \alpha\, \mathbf{L}f(x) + \beta\, \mathbf{L}g(x)$$

for all functions $f(x)$, $g(x)$ which have n derivatives on I, and any constants α and β.

Let

$$p_0(x)\, y^{(n)} + p_1(x)\, y^{(n-1)} + \cdots + p_n(x)\, y = 0 \tag{4}$$

be a homogeneous linear differential equation where the $p_i(x)$, $0 \leqq i \leqq n$, are continuous on $I = [a,b]$ and $p_0(x) > 0$ on $[a,b]$. If we introduce the variables z_j, $1 \leqq j \leqq n$, by the equations

$$z_{i+1} = y^{(i)}, \qquad 0 \leqq i \leqq n-1,$$

then (4) may be written as

$$\begin{aligned}
\frac{dz_1}{dx} &= z_2 \\
\frac{dz_2}{dx} &= z_3 \\
&\cdots\cdots\cdots \\
\frac{dz_{n-1}}{dx} &= z_n \\
\frac{dz_n}{dx} &= -\frac{p_n(x)}{p_0(x)} z_1 - \frac{p_{n-1}(x)}{p_0(x)} z_2 - \cdots - \frac{p_2(x)}{p_0(x)} z_{n-1} - \frac{p_1(x)}{p_0(x)} z_n.
\end{aligned} \tag{5}$$

More compactly, if

$$Z(x) = \{z_1(x), z_2(x), \cdots, z_n(x)\}$$

is the column vector of the z_i's and

$$\frac{dZ}{dx} = \left\{\frac{dz_1}{dx}, \frac{dz_2}{dx}, \cdots, \frac{dz_n}{dx}\right\}$$

is its derivative, then (5) may be written as

$$\frac{dZ}{dx} = P(x)\, Z \tag{6}$$

where

$$P(x) = \left\| \begin{matrix} 0 & 1 & 0 & \cdots & 0 & 0 \\ 0 & 0 & 1 & \cdots & 0 & 0 \\ \cdot & \cdot & \cdot & \cdot & \cdot & \cdot \\ 0 & 0 & 0 & \cdots & 0 & 1 \\ -\frac{p_n(x)}{p_0(x)} & -\frac{p_{n-1}(x)}{p_0(x)} & -\frac{p_{n-2}(x)}{p_0(x)} & \cdots & -\frac{p_2(x)}{p_0(x)} & -\frac{p_1(x)}{p_0(x)} \end{matrix} \right\|$$

is the matrix of the coefficients of (5). It is clear from this formulation why we must assume $p_0(x) \neq 0$ on $[a,b]$.

Let $q_{ij}(x)$, $1 \leqq i, j \leqq n$, be n^2 functions which are continuous on $I = [a,b]$. Let

$$Q(x) = \| q_{ij}(x) \|_{1 \leqq i, j \leqq n}$$

be the matrix of the $q_{ij}(x)$ where q_{ij} is the element in the ith row and jth column of Q. Then it is sometimes convenient to consider the differential equation

$$\frac{dY}{dx} = Q(x)\, Y \tag{7}$$

where $Y(x) = \{y_1(x), y_2(x), \cdots, y_n(x)\}$ is a column vector and dY/dx its derivative. Clearly (6) is a special case of (7). Hence whatever results we demonstrate for (7) are *a fortiori* true *mutatis mutandis* for (6) and hence for (4). We also call (7) a linear differential equation.

2. Existence and Uniqueness

The first and most important question to ask in connection with (1.4) is whether there actually exists a function $y(x)$ which satisfies this equation. That is, given $n+1$ functions $p_i(x)$, $0 \leqq i \leqq n$, where the $p_i(x)$ are continuous on some closed finite interval $I = [a,b]$ and $p_0(x) > 0$ on I, can we find a function $y(x)$ defined on I such that

$$\mathbf{L}y(x) = p_0(x)y^{(n)}(x) + p_1(x)y^{(n-1)}(x) + \cdots + p_n(x)y(x) \equiv 0 \quad (1)$$

for all $x \in I$? If such a function exists, its first n derivatives must exist, and from the equation

$$y^{(n)}(x) = -\frac{p_1(x)}{p_0(x)}y^{(n-1)}(x) - \frac{p_2(x)}{p_0(x)}y^{(n-2)}(x) - \cdots - \frac{p_n(x)}{p_0(x)}y(x)$$

we must also infer that $y(x) \in C^n(I)$.

Now the function identically zero on I has the property that it satisfies (1) for all $x \in I$. Also if $\varphi(x)$ is a non-identically zero function which satisfies (1), then so does $\alpha\ \varphi(x)$ where α is an arbitrary constant. Thus if we are to avoid trivial results, certain additional restrictions must be placed on candidates for solutions of (1). These restrictions take the form of boundary conditions.

Assuming for the moment that we have obtained a solution of (1), the second fundamental question is to establish, if possible, the *uniqueness* of this solution. Both these questions are definitively answered by the following theorem.

Theorem 1. Let $Q(x) = \| q_{ij}(x) \|_{1 \leqq i,j \leqq n}$ be an $n \times n$ matrix where the $q_{ij}(x)$, $1 \leqq i, j \leqq n$, are n^2 functions continuous on the closed finite interval $I = [a,b]$. Let x_0 be any point in I and let $Y_0 = \{y_{10}, y_{20}, \cdots, y_{n0}\}$ be any constant vector. Then there exists a unique continuously differentiable vector $Y(x) = \{y_1(x), y_2(x), \cdots, y_n(x)\}$ which satisfies the equation

$$\frac{dY}{dx} = Q(x)\ Y \quad (2)$$

for all $x \in I$ and furthermore has the property that

$$Y(x_0) = Y_0.$$

Proof. Suppose for the moment that such a vector function $Y(x)$ exists. Then (2) may be written as

$$Y(x) = Y_0 + \int_{x_0}^{x} Q(\xi)\,Y(\xi)\,d\xi. \quad (3)$$

Conversely, suppose $Y(x)$ is a continuous function which satisfies (3). Then the continuity of $Q(x)\,Y(x)$ implies the differentiability of

$$\int_{x_0}^{x} Q(\xi)\,Y(\xi)\,d\xi.$$

Since a constant, Y_0, is certainly differentiable, (3) now implies the differentiability of $Y(x)$. Differentiating (3) we obtain (2). Also from (3)

$$Y(x_0) = Y_0 + \int_{x_0}^{x_0} Q(\xi)\,Y(\xi)\,d\xi = Y_0.$$

Thus if we can find a vector $Y(x)$ continuous on I which satisfies (3), then *a fortiori* it is a solution of (2) which takes on the prescribed boundary values Y_0.

We shall first find a continuous vector $Y(x)$ which satisfies (3) and then prove that it is unique. Toward this end let us introduce certain notations. Let

$$|Q(x)| = \max_i \sum_{j=1}^{n} |q_{ij}(x)|, \qquad x \in I \tag{4}$$

and let

$$\|Q\| = \operatorname*{l.u.b.}_{x \in I} |Q(x)| \tag{5}$$

for any square matrix $Q(x)$ with entries continuous on I. Then $|Q(x)|$ is a scalar function of x and $\|Q\|$ is a constant. We shall call $\|Q\|$ the *norm* of $Q(x)$. If $Z(x) = \{z_1(x), z_2(x), \cdots, z_n(x)\}$ is a vector continuous on I, then we define $|Z(x)|$ as

$$|Z(x)| = \max_i |z_i(x)|, \qquad x \in I \tag{6}$$

and

$$\|Z\| = \operatorname*{l.u.b.}_{x \in I} |e^{-\alpha|x-x_0|}Z(x)| \tag{7}$$

for some positive constant α. We call $\|Z\|$ the *norm* of Z.

From (4) and (6) we readily infer

$$|Q(x)Z(x)| \leqq |Q(x)|\,|Z(x)| \tag{8}$$

since

$$\begin{aligned} |Q(x)Z(x)| &= \max_i \left| \sum_{j=1}^{n} q_{ij}(x) z_j(x) \right| \\ &\leqq \max_i \sum_j |q_{ij}(x)|\,|z_j(x)| \\ &\leqq \left[\max_i \sum_j |q_{ij}(x)|\right] \left[\max_j |z_j(x)|\right] = |Q(x)|\,|Z(x)|. \end{aligned}$$

Also from (5) and (7) we shall prove

$$\boldsymbol{|}QZ\boldsymbol{|} \leqq \boldsymbol{|}Q\boldsymbol{|}\,\boldsymbol{|}Z\boldsymbol{|}. \tag{9}$$

For

$$\begin{aligned} \boldsymbol{|}QZ\boldsymbol{|} &= \underset{x \in I}{\text{l.u.b.}} \left| e^{-\alpha|x-x_0|} Q(x)Z(x) \right| \\ &\leqq \left[\underset{x \in I}{\text{l.u.b.}} |Q(x)|\right] \left[\underset{x \in I}{\text{l.u.b.}}\ e^{-\alpha|x-x_0|}\,|Z(x)|\right] = \boldsymbol{|}Q\boldsymbol{|}\,\boldsymbol{|}Z\boldsymbol{|}. \end{aligned}$$

Finally we shall establish the integral inequality

$$\left| \int_{x_0}^{x} Z(\xi) d\xi \right| \leqq \int_{x_0}^{x} |Z(\xi)|\,|d\xi|. \tag{10}$$

For

$$\begin{aligned} \left| \int_{x_0}^{x} Z(\xi) d\xi \right| &= \max_i \left| \int_{x_0}^{x} z_i(\xi) d\xi \right| \\ &\leqq \max_i \int_{x_3}^{x} |z_i(\xi)|\,|d\xi| \\ &\leqq \int_{x_0}^{x} \max_i |z_i(\xi)|\,|d\xi| = \int_{x_0}^{x} |Z(\xi)|\,|d\xi|. \end{aligned}$$

Now define the operator $\mathbf{K}$ as

$$\mathbf{K}Z(x) = \int_{x_0}^{x} Q(\xi)Z(\xi)\, d\xi. \tag{11}$$

Let x' be any point in I. Then

$$
\begin{aligned}
|\mathbf{K}Z(x')| &= \left|\int_{x_0}^{x'} Q(\xi)Z(\xi)\,d\xi\right| \\
&\leqq \int_{x_0}^{x'} |Q(\xi)Z(\xi)|\,|d\xi| \\
&\leqq \int_{x_0}^{x'} |Q(\xi)|\,|Z(\xi)|\,|d\xi|
\end{aligned} \tag{12}
$$

by (10) and (8). Multiply both sides of (12) by $e^{-\alpha|x'-x_0|}$. Then

$$
\begin{aligned}
&|\mathbf{K}Z(x')|\,e^{-\alpha|x'-x_0|} \\
&\quad \leqq \int_{x_0}^{x'} |Q(\xi)|\,|e^{-\alpha|\xi-x_0|}Z(\xi)|\,e^{-\alpha|x'-x_0|}\,e^{\alpha|\xi-x_0|}\,|d\xi|.
\end{aligned} \tag{13}
$$

But

$$e^{-\alpha(|x'-x_0|-|\xi-x_0|)} = e^{-\alpha|x'-\xi|}$$

since ξ is between x_0 and x'. Thus, by definition of norms, (13) becomes

$$|\mathbf{K}Z(x')|e^{-\alpha|x'-x_0|} \leqq \|Q\|\,\|Z\|\int_{x_0}^{x'} e^{-\alpha|x'-\xi|}\,|d\xi|. \tag{14}$$

Now

$$\int_{x_0}^{x'} e^{-\alpha|x'-\xi|}\,|d\xi| = \frac{1}{\alpha}\left[1-e^{-\alpha|x'-x_0|}\right] \leqq \frac{1}{\alpha}.$$

Thus from (14)

$$e^{-\alpha|x'-x_0|}\,|\mathbf{K}Z(x')| \leqq \frac{1}{\alpha}\,\|Q\|\,\|Z\|. \tag{15}$$

Since the right-hand side of (15) is independent of x',

$$\|\mathbf{K}Z\| = \underset{x'\in I}{\text{l.u.b.}}\left|e^{-\alpha|x'-x_0|}\,\mathbf{K}Z(x')\right| \leqq \frac{1}{\alpha}\,\|Q\|\,\|Z\|$$

or

$$\|\mathbf{K}Z\| \leqq \frac{1}{\alpha} \|Q\| \; \|Z\|. \tag{16}$$

Now (16) is valid for any $\alpha > 0$. Choose a θ, $0 < \theta < 1$, and then choose an α such that

$$\alpha > \frac{\|Q\|}{\theta}.$$

Then (16) becomes

$$\|\mathbf{K}Z\| \leqq \theta \|Z\|, \qquad 0 < \theta < 1. \tag{17}$$

We shall now construct a sequence of continuous vectors $\{Y_p(x)\}$ which converge uniformly on I to a solution of (3). Let

$$\begin{aligned} Y_0(x) &= Y_0 \\ Y_p(x) &= Y_0 + \mathbf{K}Y_{p-1}(x), \qquad p > 0. \end{aligned} \tag{18}$$

Then

$$Y_1 - Y_0 = \mathbf{K}Y_0$$

and

$$\begin{aligned} Y_2 - Y_1 &= \mathbf{K}Y_1 - \mathbf{K}Y_0 \\ &= \mathbf{K}[Y_0 + \mathbf{K}Y_0] - \mathbf{K}Y_0 \\ &= \mathbf{K}\mathbf{K}Y_0 \end{aligned}$$

which we shall write symbolically as $\mathbf{K}^2 Y_0$. Now assume

$$Y_p - Y_{p-1} = \mathbf{K}^{p-1} Y_0.$$

Then by induction

$$\begin{aligned} Y_{p+1} - Y_p &= (Y_0 + \mathbf{K}Y_p) - (Y_0 + \mathbf{K}Y_{p-1}) \\ &= \mathbf{K}(Y_p - Y_{p-1}) = \mathbf{K}(\mathbf{K}^{p-1}Y_0) = \mathbf{K}^p Y_0. \end{aligned}$$

Consider now $Y_p - Y_q$ with $p > q$. Then

$$\begin{aligned} Y_p - Y_q &= (Y_p - Y_{p-1}) + (Y_{p-1} - Y_{p-2}) + \cdots + (Y_{q+1} - Y_q) \\ &= \mathbf{K}^{p-1}Y_0 + \mathbf{K}^{p-2}Y_0 + \cdots + \mathbf{K}^q Y_0 \\ &= (\mathbf{K}^{p-1} + \mathbf{K}^{p-2} + \cdots + \mathbf{K}^q) Y_0. \end{aligned} \tag{19}$$

But from (17),

$$\|\mathbf{K}^2 Z\| = \|\mathbf{K}(\mathbf{K}Z)\| \leqq \theta \|\mathbf{K}Z\| \leqq \theta^2 \|Z\|$$

and by another elementary induction

$$\|\mathbf{K}^m Z\| \leqq \theta^m \|Z\|. \tag{20}$$

Using this result in (19) implies

$$\|Y_p - Y_q\| \leqq (\theta^{p-1} + \theta^{p-2} + \cdots + \theta^q)\,\|Y_0\| \tag{21}$$

since the norm of a vector satisfies the triangle inequality. But $0 < \theta < 1$. Thus (21) implies

$$\|Y_p - Y_q\| \leqq \frac{\theta^q}{1-\theta}\,\|Y_0\|. \tag{22}$$

The right-hand side of (22) approaches zero as q (and hence p) increase without limit. Thus the sequence $\{Y_m(x)\}$ converges in norm, and hence uniformly on I. Since $Y_m(x)$ is continuous on I, the sequence converges to a continuous function, say $Y(x)$:

$$\lim_{m\to\infty} Y_m(x) = Y(x).$$

Thus

$$\lim_{m\to\infty} Q(x)\,Y_m(x) = Q(x)\lim_{m\to\infty} Y_m(x) = Q(x)\,Y(x)$$

is also continuous on I. From (18) follows

$$\begin{aligned} Y(x) &= \lim_{m\to\infty} Y_m(x) = \lim_{m\to\infty} Y_0 + \lim_{m\to\infty} \mathbf{K}\,Y_{m-1}(x) \\ &= Y_0 + \lim_{m\to\infty}\int_{x_0}^{x} Q(\xi)\,Y_{m-1}(\xi)\,d\xi \\ &= Y_0 + \int_{x_0}^{x} \lim_{m\to\infty} Q(\xi)\,Y_{m-1}(\xi)\,d\xi \\ &= Y_0 + \int_{x_0}^{x} Q(\xi)\,Y(\xi)\,d\xi. \end{aligned}$$

Thus the limit function $Y(x)$ is a solution of the integral equation (3) and *a fortiori* of the differential equation (2) with the initial condition $Y(x_0) = Y_0$.

We must now prove that $Y(x)$ is unique. Let $V(x)$ be any solution of (3) and let the Picard iterants $Y_m(x)$ be as defined in (18). Then

$$\begin{aligned} V &= Y_0 + \mathbf{K}V \\ Y_m &= Y_0 + \mathbf{K}Y_{m-1} \end{aligned} \tag{23}$$

and

$$\begin{aligned} V - Y_m &= \mathbf{K}V - \mathbf{K}Y_{m-1} \\ &= \mathbf{K}V - \mathbf{K}(Y_0 + \mathbf{K}Y_{m-2}) \\ &= \mathbf{K}(V - Y_0) - \mathbf{K}^2 Y_{m-2} \\ &= \mathbf{K}^2 V - \mathbf{K}^2 Y_{m-2} \end{aligned}$$

by (23). By induction we establish the result

$$V - Y_m = \mathbf{K}^m(V - Y_0)$$

or

$$\| V - Y_m \| \leqq \theta^m \| V - Y_0 \| \tag{24}$$

by (20). But the right-hand side of (24) approaches zero as m increases without limit. Thus $\{Y_m(x)\}$ converges uniformly on I to $V(x)$ and our solution is unique.

3. The Wronskian

In this and the next section we wish to recount some elementary properties of the solutions of linear differential equations. Deeper theorems will be analyzed in subsequent chapters. Some of the most interesting results center about the concept of *Wronskian* which we now proceed to define.

Let $f_j(x)$, $1 \leqq j \leqq p$, be p functions of class $C^{p-1}(I)$ where I is the closed finite interval $[a,b]$. Let $\Delta(x)$ be the $p \times p$ matrix

$$\Delta(x) = \| f_j^{(i-1)}(x) \|_{1 \leqq i,j \leqq p}$$

where $f_j^{(i-1)}$ is the element in the ith row and jth column of $\Delta(x)$. Then we call $\Delta(x)$ the *Wronskian matrix* of the $f_j(x)$. The determinant $D(x)$ of $\Delta(x)$ is called the Wronskian determinant or simply the *Wronskian* of the $f_j(x)$. If $D(x) \neq 0$ for all $x \in I$, then we assert that the $f_j(x)$ are *linearly independent*. For suppose there existed constants $c_1, c_2, \cdots, c_p$ not all zero such that

$$c_1 f_1(x) + c_2 f_2(x) + \cdots + c_p f_p(x) = 0 \tag{1}$$

identically for all $x \in I$. If we differentiate (1) $p-1$ times, we obtain, together with (1), the equation

$$\Delta(x)\, C = 0$$

where $C = \{c_1, c_2, \cdots, c_p\}$ is the column vector of constants. But $\Delta(x)$ is non-singular for all x in I. Hence by Cramer's rule $C = 0$, a contradiction.

Let

$$p_0(x)\, y^{(n)} + p_1(x)\, y^{(n-1)} + \cdots + p_n(x)\, y = 0 \tag{2}$$

be a linear differential equation where the $p_i(x)$, $0 \leqq i \leqq n$, are continuous on $I=[a,b]$ and $p_0(x) > 0$ on $[a,b]$. If we introduce the variables z_j, $1 \leqq j \leqq n$, by the equations

$$z_{i+1} = y^{(i)}, \qquad 0 \leqq i \leqq n-1, \tag{3}$$

then (2) may be written as the first-order system given in (1.5). But this is the same type of differential equation as was discussed in Section 2. Hence if $Z_0 = \{z_{10}, z_{20}, \cdots, z_{n0}\}$ is any constant vector and x_0 is any point in the closed interval I, then there exists a unique, continuously differentiable vector $Z(x) = \{z_1(x), z_2(x), \cdots, z_n(x)\}$ which satisfies (1.5) for all $x \in I$ and further has the property that $Z(x_0) = Z_0$. Thus, interpreted in terms of the $y^{(i)}$, we may state the following theorem:

Theorem 2. Let

$$\mathbf{L} = p_0(x)\frac{d^n}{dx^n} + p_1(x)\frac{d^{n-1}}{dx^{n-1}} + \cdots + p_n(x)\cdot \tag{4}$$

be a linear differential operator where the $p_i(x)$, $0 \leqq i \leqq n$, are continuous on the closed finite interval I and $p_0(x) > 0$ on I. Let a_1, $a_2, \cdots, a_n$ be any n constants and let x_0 be any point in I. Then there exists one and only one function $y(x)$ with the properties that

$$\mathbf{L}y(x) \equiv 0$$

and

$$y^{(k-1)}(x_0) = a_k, \qquad 1 \leqq k \leqq n.$$

Let $A = \| a_{ij} \|_{1 \leqq i,j \leqq n}$ be a square matrix of constants. Let $\varphi_i(x)$, $1 \leqq i \leqq n$, be n solutions of $\mathbf{L}y = 0$ with the property that

$$\varphi_j^{(i-1)}(x_0) = a_{ij}, \qquad 1 \leqq i, j \leqq n,$$

for some x_0 in I. Let

$$\Omega(x) = \| \varphi_j^{(i-1)}(x) \|_{1 \leqq i, j \leqq n} = \left\| \begin{matrix} \varphi_1(x) & \varphi_2(x) & \cdots & \varphi_n(x) \\ \varphi_1'(x) & \varphi_2'(x) & \cdots & \varphi_n'(x) \\ \cdot & \cdot & \cdot & \cdot \\ \varphi_1^{(n-1)}(x) & \varphi_2^{(n-1)}(x) & \cdots & \varphi_n^{(n-1)}(x) \end{matrix} \right\|$$

be the Wronskian matrix of the $\varphi_i(x)$ and

$$W(x) = \det \Omega(x),$$

the determinant of $\Omega(x)$, be the Wronskian. If we differentiate $W(x)$ we see that $W'(x)$ is identical with $W(x)$ except that the last row is replaced by $\{\varphi_1^{(n)}(x), \varphi_2^{(n)}(x), \cdots, \varphi_n^{(n)}(x)\}$. But $\mathbf{L}\varphi_j(x) = 0$, $1 \leqq j \leqq n$. Therefore, from (2),

$$\varphi_j^{(n)}(x) = -\frac{p_1(x)}{p_0(x)} \varphi_j^{(n-1)}(x) - \frac{p_2(x)}{p_0(x)} \varphi_j^{(n-2)}(x) - \cdots - \frac{p_n(x)}{p_0(x)} \varphi_j(x), \ 1 \leqq j \leqq n.$$

Thus

$$\frac{d}{dx} W(x) = -\frac{p_1(x)}{p_0(x)} W(x)$$

and

$$W(x) = W(x_0)\, e^{-\int_{x_0}^{x} \frac{p_1(\xi)}{p_0(\xi)} d\xi}.$$

By construction,

$$\Omega(x_0) = \| \varphi_j^{(i-1)}(x_0) \|_{1 \leqq i, j \leqq n} = A$$

and it follows that

$$W(x) = (\det A)\, e^{-\int_{x_0}^{x} \frac{p_1(\xi)}{p_0(\xi)} d\xi}. \tag{5}$$

Hence we see that $W(x)$ is either never zero or else identically zero for all x in I depending on whether A is non-singular or singular. Summarizing:

Theorem 3. Let $\{\varphi_j(x) | 1 \leqq j \leqq n\}$ be n solutions of $\mathbf{L}y = 0$. Then the Wronskian $W(x) = \det \| \varphi_j^{(i-1)}(x) \|_{1 \leqq i, j \leqq n}$ of the $\varphi_j(x)$ satisfies the differential equation

$$p_0(x)\, W'(x) + p_1(x)\, W(x) = 0$$

and is either identically zero on I [if $W(x_0)=0$], or never zero on I [if $W(x_0) \neq 0$].

4. Properties of the Wronskian

As before, let us consider the homogeneous linear differential equation

$$\mathbf{L}y = p_0(x)\, y^{(n)} + p_1(x)\, y^{(n-1)} + \cdots + p_n(x)\, y = 0, \tag{1}$$

where the $p_i(x), 0 \leqq i \leqq n$, are continuous on $I=[a,b]$ and $p_0(x) > 0$ on $[a,b]$. Let $\{\varphi_j(x)|1 \leqq j \leqq n\}$ be n solutions of (1). We assert that the following three statements are equivalent:

(i) The $\varphi_j(x)$, $1 \leqq j \leqq n$, are linearly independent on I.
(ii) Any solution of $\mathbf{L}y=0$ may be written as a linear combination of the $\varphi_j(x)$.
(iii) The Wronskian of the $\varphi_j(x)$ is never zero on I.

The introductory remarks of the preceding section show us that (iii) implies (i). We write this symbolically as

$$\text{(iii)} \Rightarrow \text{(i)}. \tag{2}$$

In Theorem 4 below we shall prove that

$$\text{(iii)} \Rightarrow \text{(ii)}. \tag{3}$$

Theorem 6 will show that

$$\text{(ii)} \Rightarrow \text{(iii)} \tag{4}$$

and Theorem 7 will establish

$$\text{(i)} \Rightarrow \text{(iii)}. \tag{5}$$

Clearly (2), (3), (4), and (5) establish the complete equivalence of (i), (ii), and (iii).

To prove (3) we first exhibit a particular set of solutions of (1) with non-zero Wronskian which enjoys property (ii). Let $\{\chi_j(x)|1 \leqq j \leqq n\}$ be n solutions of $\mathbf{L}y=0$ so chosen that

$$\chi_j^{(i-1)}(x_0) = \delta_{ij}, \qquad 1 \leqq i, j \leqq n, \tag{6}$$

for some $x_0 \in I$ where δ_{ij} is the Kronecker delta. Then the Wronskian $W_\chi(x)$ of the $\chi_j(x)$ is never zero on I since $W_\chi(x_0)=1 \neq 0$ (cf. Theorem 3). Now suppose $y(x)$ is a solution of $\mathbf{L}y=0$ which assumes the values

$$y^{(i-1)}(x_0) = c_i, \qquad 1 \leqq i \leqq n.$$

Then $y(x)$ may be written as a linear combination of the $\chi_j(x)$, namely,

$$y(x) = c_1 \chi_1(x) + c_2 \chi_2(x) + \cdots + c_n \chi_n(x). \tag{7}$$

Suppose now that $\varphi_j(x)$, $1 \leqq j \leqq n$, are n solutions of $\mathbf{L}y=0$ with non-singular Wronskian matrix $\Omega_\varphi(x)$. We wish to show that any solution of (1) may be written as a linear combination of the $\varphi_j(x)$. This will establish (3). By virtue of (7) we may write

$$\Phi(x) = \tilde{\Omega}_\varphi(x_0)\, X(x) \tag{8}$$

where $\Phi(x)=\{\varphi_1(x), \varphi_2(x), \cdots, \varphi_n(x)\}$ and $X(x)=\{\chi_1(x), \chi_2(x), \cdots, \chi_n(x)\}$ are column vectors and $\tilde{\Omega}_\varphi$ is the transpose (rows and columns interchanged) of the Wronskian matrix Ω_φ of Φ. Since $\det \tilde{\Omega}_\varphi(x_0) \neq 0$, we may write from (8) that

$$X(x) = \tilde{\Omega}_\varphi^{-1}(x_0)\, \Phi(x).$$

Equation (7) then implies that any solution of $\mathbf{L}y=0$ may be written as a linear combination of the $\varphi_j(x)$. Hence we have the following theorem:

Theorem 4. Let $\varphi_j(x)$, $1 \leqq j \leqq n$, be any n solutions of $\mathbf{L}y=0$ whose Wronskian does not vanish on I. Then *any* solution of $\mathbf{L}y=0$ may be written as a linear combination of the $\varphi_j(x)$.

We shall call any set of n solutions of $\mathbf{L}y=0$ whose Wronskian does not vanish on I a *fundamental system* or a *fundamental set of solutions* of $\mathbf{L}y=0$.

As an immediate consequence of this definition we observe that:

Theorem 5. If $\Phi(x)=\{\varphi_1(x), \varphi_2(x), \cdots, \varphi_n(x)\}$ and $\Psi(x)=\{\psi_1(x), \psi_2(x), \cdots, \psi_n(x)\}$ are two fundamental systems of solutions, then the

Wronskians $W_\varphi(x)$ and $W_\psi(x)$ of Φ and Ψ respectively differ by a non-zero multiplicative constant.

Proof. From (3.5)

$$W_\varphi(x) = k\, W_\psi(x)$$

where $k = W_\varphi(x_0)/W_\psi(x_0) \neq 0$.

We turn our attention now to the problem of establishing (4). That is, if $\varphi_j(x)$, $1 \leqq j \leqq n$, are n solutions of (1) with the property that *any* solution of (1) may be written as a linear combination of the $\varphi_j(x)$, then the Wronskian of the $\varphi_j(x)$ is unequal to zero.

Suppose the $\varphi_j(x)$, $1 \leqq j \leqq n$, enjoy property (ii). Then in particular the $\chi_j(x)$, $1 \leqq j \leqq n$, [cf. (6)] may be written:

$$X(x) = A\, \Phi(x) \tag{9}$$

where A is a constant matrix. But *any* solution of $\mathbf{L}y=0$ may be written as a linear combination of the $\chi_j(x)$, [cf. (7)]. Thus, in particular

$$\Phi(x) = B\, X(x). \tag{10}$$

These last two equations imply

$$X(x) = AB\, X(x)$$

or

$$AB = E$$

where $E = \|\delta_{ij}\|_{1 \leqq i,j \leqq n}$ is the $n \times n$ identity matrix. Thus $\det A \neq 0$, $\det B \neq 0$, and $A = B^{-1}$.

From (9)

$$\Omega_\chi(x) = \Omega_\varphi(x)\, \tilde{A} \tag{11}$$

where $\tilde{A}$ is the transpose of A and Ω_χ and Ω_φ are the Wronskian matrices of X and Φ respectively. Thus (11) implies

$$\det \Omega_\chi(x) = (\det \Omega_\varphi(x))\,(\det \tilde{A}).$$

Since $\det \Omega_\chi(x) \neq 0$ and $\det \tilde{A} = \det A \neq 0$, we infer that $\det \Omega_\varphi(x) \neq 0$. That is, the Wronskian of $\Phi(x)$ is unequal to zero and hence the $\varphi_j(x)$, $1 \leqq j \leqq n$, form a fundamental system of solutions of $\mathbf{L}y=0$. Whence we have:

Theorem 6. If $\varphi_j(x)$, $1 \leqq j \leqq n$, are n solutions of $\mathbf{L}y=0$ with the property that every solution of $\mathbf{L}y=0$ may be written as a linear combination of the $\varphi_j(x)$, then the $\varphi_j(x)$ form a fundamental set of solutions of $\mathbf{L}y=0$.

Finally we shall prove (5), that is, that the linear independence of the $\varphi_j(x)$ implies the non-vanishing of the Wronskian. This result will then complete the proof of the equivalence of (i), (ii), and (iii).

Theorem 7. Let z_j, $1 \leqq j \leqq n$, be n linearly independent solutions of $\mathbf{L}y=0$. Then the Wronskian of the z_j is unequal to zero on I.

Proof. Let $\Phi(x)=\{\varphi_1(x), \varphi_2(x), \cdots, \varphi_n(x)\}$ be a fundamental set of solutions of $\mathbf{L}y=0$. Then by Theorem 4 there exists a constant matrix C such that

$$Z(x) = C\,\Phi(x) \tag{12}$$

where $Z(x)=\{z_1(x), z_2(x), \cdots, z_n(x)\}$.

Let $B=\{b_1, b_2, \cdots, b_n\}$ be a column vector of constants and $\tilde{B}$, its transpose, a row vector. Now suppose

$$\tilde{B}C\,\Phi(x) = 0. \tag{13}$$

Since $\Phi(x)$ is a fundamental system, the $\varphi_j(x)$ are linearly independent and hence $\tilde{B}C$ must be the zero vector. We assert that det $C \neq 0$. For if det $C=0$, there would exist a $\tilde{B} \neq 0$ such that $\tilde{B}C=0$. But from (12) and (13)

$$\tilde{B}\,Z(x) = 0$$

and since the $z_j(x)$ are linearly independent by hypothesis we must have $\tilde{B}=0$. Thus det $C \neq 0$.

Now from (12)

$$W_z(x) = (\det C)\; W_\varphi(x)$$

where $W_z(x)$ and $W_\varphi(x)$ are the Wronskians of Z and Φ respectively. Since det $C \neq 0$ and $W_\varphi(x) \neq 0$ by construction, we infer that $W_z(x) \neq 0$, as we wished to prove.

2

THE ADJOINT OPERATOR

1. Lagrange's Identity

The concept of integrating factor plays an important role in the theory of first order equations. In an attempt to generalize this idea to nth order equations we are led to the definition of the *adjoint operator*. This in turn leads to the important identity known as *Green's formula* as well as *Lagrange's identity* and the *Lagrange bilinear concomitant*. In this section we shall show how the adjoint operator arises in a natural fashion, and establish the basic formulas.

Let $u(x)$ and $v(x)$ be of class C^k on some interval I. Let x_0 and x be points in I. Then by successive integration by parts the expression

$$\int_{x_0}^{x} v(\xi)\, u^{(k)}(\xi)\, d\xi$$

may be transformed into one in which the differentiation is transferred to $v(\xi)$:

$$\begin{aligned}\int_{x_0}^{x} v(\xi)\, u^{(k)}(\xi)\, d\xi &= \int_{x_0}^{x} v(\xi)\, du^{(k-1)}(\xi) = v(\xi)\, u^{(k-1)}(\xi)\Big|_{x_0}^{x} - \int_{x_0}^{x} v'(\xi)\, u^{(k-1)}(\xi)\, d\xi \\ &= v(\xi)\, u^{(k-1)}(\xi)\Big|_{x_0}^{x} - v'(\xi)\, u^{(k-2)}(\xi)\Big|_{x_0}^{x} \\ &\quad + \int_{x_0}^{x} v''(\xi)\, u^{(k-2)}(\xi)\, d\xi \end{aligned} \tag{1}$$

$$= \sum_{\alpha=0}^{k-1} (-1)^{\alpha} v^{(\alpha)}(\xi)\, u^{(k-1-\alpha)}(\xi) \Big|_{x_0}^{x} + (-1)^k \int_{x_0}^{x} v^{(k)}(\xi)\, u(\xi)\, d\xi.$$

Now let

$$\mathbf{L} = p_0(x) \frac{d^n}{dx^n} + p_1(x) \frac{d^{n-1}}{dx^{n-1}} + \cdots + p_n(x).$$

where $p_i(x) \in C^{n-i}$, $0 \leqq i \leqq n$, on some interval I. Then we may write

$$\mathbf{L}u(x) = \sum_{k=0}^{n} p_{n-k}(x)\, u^{(k)}(x)$$

for any function $u(x)$ of class $C^n(I)$. From (1)

$$\begin{aligned} \int_{x_0}^{x} v(\xi)\, \mathbf{L}u(\xi)\, d\xi &= \sum_{k=0}^{n} \int_{x_0}^{x} [v(\xi)\, p_{n-k}(\xi)]\, u^{(k)}(\xi)\, d\xi \\ &= \sum_{k=0}^{n} \Big\{ \sum_{\alpha=0}^{k-1} (-1)^{\alpha} [v(\xi)\, p_{n-k}(\xi)]^{(\alpha)}\, u^{(k-1-\alpha)}(\xi) \Big|_{x_0}^{x} \\ &\qquad + (-1)^k \int_{x_0}^{x} [v(\xi) p_{n-k}(\xi)]^{(k)}\, u(\xi)\, d\xi \Big\}. \end{aligned} \tag{2}$$

Let

$$\begin{aligned} \mathbf{L}^* v &= (-1)^n \frac{d^n}{dx^n}(p_0 v) + (-1)^{n-1} \frac{d^{n-1}}{dx^{n-1}}(p_1 v) \\ &\quad + \cdots + (-1) \frac{d}{dx}(p_{n-1} v) + (p_n v). \end{aligned} \tag{3}$$

Then (2) becomes

$$\int_{x_0}^{x} v(\xi)\, \mathbf{L}u(\xi)\, d\xi = \pi[u(\xi), v(\xi)] \Big|_{x_0}^{x} + \int_{x_0}^{x} u(\xi)\, \mathbf{L}^* v(\xi)\, d\xi$$

or

$$\int_{x_0}^{x} [v(\xi)\, \mathbf{L}u(\xi) - u(\xi)\, \mathbf{L}^* v(\xi)]\, d\xi = \pi[u(\xi), v(\xi)] \Big|_{x_0}^{x}. \tag{4}$$

The operator $\mathbf{L}^*$ defined by (3) is called the *adjoint* of $\mathbf{L}$. The expression

$$\begin{aligned}\pi[u, v] &= \sum_{k=0}^{n}\sum_{\alpha=0}^{k-1}(-1)^{\alpha}[vp_{n-k}]^{(\alpha)}\,u^{(k-1-\alpha)}\\ &= [vp_{n-1}]\,u\\ &\quad + [vp_{n-2}]\,u' - [vp_{n-2}]'\,u\\ &\quad + [vp_{n-3}]\,u'' - [vp_{n-3}]'\,u' + [vp_{n-3}]''\,u\\ &\quad + \cdot \quad \cdot \quad \cdot \quad \cdot \quad \cdot \quad \cdot \quad \cdot \quad \cdot\\ &\quad + [vp_0]\,u^{(n-1)} - [vp_0]'\,u^{(n-2)} + \cdots + (-1)^{n-1}[vp_0]^{(n-1)}\,u\end{aligned} \tag{5}$$

is called the *Lagrange bilinear concomitant*. Equation (4) is known as *Green's formula* and if we differentiate (4) we obtain *Lagrange's identity:*

$$v(x)\,\mathbf{L}u(x) - u(x)\,\mathbf{L}^*v(x) = \frac{d}{dx}\,\pi[u(x), v(x)]. \tag{6}$$

2. Algebraic Properties

We shall have occasion to use the adjoint operator in almost every succeeding chapter of this book. It is therefore appropriate that initially we examine some of its formal algebraic properties. If $\mathbf{L}$ and $\mathbf{M}$ are linear differential operators we shall show, essentially, that

$$\begin{aligned}(\mathbf{L} + \mathbf{M})^* &= \mathbf{L}^* + \mathbf{M}^*\\ \mathbf{L}^{**} &= \mathbf{L}\\ (\mathbf{LM})^* &= \mathbf{M}^*\mathbf{L}^*.\end{aligned}$$

To establish the precise conditions under which the above formulas are valid we start by considering

$$\mathbf{L} = p_0(x)\frac{d^n}{dx^n} + p_1(x)\frac{d^{n-1}}{dx^{n-1}} + \cdots + p_n(x)\cdot$$

and

$$\mathbf{M} = q_0(x)\frac{d^m}{dx^m} + q_1(x)\frac{d^{m-1}}{dx^{m-1}} + \cdots + q_m(x)\cdot$$

where $p_i(x) \in C^{n-i}$, $0 \leqq i \leqq n$, and $q_j(x) \in C^{m-j}$, $0 \leqq j \leqq m$, on some interval I. Then it is easy to see that

$$(\mathbf{L} + \mathbf{M})^* = \mathbf{L}^* + \mathbf{M}^*. \tag{1}$$

For if $N = \max(n,m)$ and we define $p_i(x)$ and $q_j(x)$ as identically zero for i and j negative, then

$$(\mathbf{L} + \mathbf{M})u = \sum_{i=0}^{N} [p_{n-i}(x) + q_{m-i}(x)]\, u^{(i)}(x)$$

for any $u \in C^N(I)$. Thus

$$\begin{aligned}
(\mathbf{L} + \mathbf{M})^*u \quad & \sum_{i=0}^{N} (-1)^i[(p_{n-i} + q_{m-i})u]^{(i)} \\
&= \sum_{i=0}^{N} (-1)^i[(p_{n-i})u + (q_{m-i})u]^{(i)} \\
&= \sum_{i=0}^{n} (-1)^i(p_{n-i}u)^{(i)} + \sum_{i=0}^{m} (-1)^i(q_{m-i}u)^{(i)} \\
&= \mathbf{L}^*u + \mathbf{M}^*u
\end{aligned}$$

and (1) is verified.

Next we show that $\mathbf{L}$ is reflexive, that is, that

$$\mathbf{L}^{**} = \mathbf{L}. \tag{2}$$

Let

$$\mathbf{L}_k = p_{n-k}\frac{d^k}{dx^k}, \qquad 0 \leqq k \leqq n.$$

Then

$$\mathbf{L} = \sum_{k=0}^{n} \mathbf{L}_k$$

and by (1)

$$\mathbf{L}^* = \sum_{k=0}^{n} \mathbf{L}_k^*. \tag{3}$$

Again applying (1), this time to (3), we obtain

$$\mathbf{L}^{**} = \sum_{k=0}^{n} \mathbf{L}_k^{**}. \tag{4}$$

Now suppose we can prove that $\mathbf{L}_k^{**} = \mathbf{L}_k$. Then (4) becomes

$$\mathbf{L}^{**} = \sum_{k=0}^{n} \mathbf{L}_k = \mathbf{L}$$

which is (2). Thus we need only prove

$$\mathbf{L}_k^{**} = \mathbf{L}_k, \qquad 0 \leqq k \leqq n.$$

Since

$$\mathbf{L}_k u = p_{n-k} u^{(k)}, \qquad 0 \leqq k \leqq n,$$

we have

$$\mathbf{L}_k^* u = (-1)^k (p_{n-k} u)^{(k)} = (-1)^k \sum_{\alpha=0}^{k} \binom{k}{\alpha} p_{n-k}^{(k-\alpha)} u^{(\alpha)}$$

by definition of the adjoint. And

$$\mathbf{L}_k^{**} u = (-1)^k \sum_{\alpha=0}^{k} (-1)^\alpha \binom{k}{\alpha} (p_{n-k}^{(k-\alpha)} u)^{(\alpha)},$$

again by definition of the adjoint. Expanding $(p_{n-k}^{(k-\alpha)} u)^{(\alpha)}$ we obtain

$$\mathbf{L}_k^{**} u = (-1)^k \sum_{\alpha=0}^{k} \sum_{\beta=0}^{\alpha} (-1)^\alpha \binom{k}{\alpha} \binom{\alpha}{\beta} p_{n-k}^{(k-\beta)} u^{(\beta)}.$$

Interchange the order of summation:

$$\mathbf{L}_k^{**} u = (-1)^k \sum_{\beta=0}^{k} \left[\sum_{\alpha=\beta}^{k} (-1)^\alpha \binom{k}{\alpha} \binom{\alpha}{\beta} \right] p_{n-k}^{(k-\beta)} u^{(\beta)}.$$

If we make the change $i = \alpha - \beta$ of dummy index of summation, then

$$\sum_{\alpha=\beta}^{k} (-1)^\alpha \binom{k}{\alpha} \binom{\alpha}{\beta} = (-1)^\beta \binom{k}{\beta} \sum_{i=0}^{k-\beta} (-1)^i \binom{k-\beta}{i}. \tag{5}$$

By the binomial theorem

$$0 = (1-1)^{k-\beta} = \sum_{i=0}^{k-\beta} (-1)^i \binom{k-\beta}{i}, \qquad \beta \neq k. \tag{6}$$

Hence

$$\mathbf{L}_k^{**} u = (-1)^k \sum_{\alpha=k}^{k} (-1)^\alpha \binom{k}{\alpha} \binom{\alpha}{k} p_{n-k} u^{(k)}$$

$$= (-1)^k (-1)^k \binom{k}{k} \binom{k}{k} p_{n-k} u^{(k)} = \mathbf{L}_k u,$$

and (4) is established.

In future chapters we shall discuss further the algebra of differential operators. For the present we shall define $\mathbf{LM}$ where $\mathbf{L}$ and $\mathbf{M}$ are linear differential operators and show that

$$(\mathbf{LM})^* = \mathbf{M}^* \mathbf{L}^*. \tag{7}$$

Let

$$\mathbf{L} = p_0(x)\frac{d^n}{dx^n} + p_1(x)\frac{d^{n-1}}{dx^{n-1}} + \cdots + p_n(x)\cdot$$

and

$$\mathbf{M} = q_0(x)\frac{d^m}{dx^m} + q_1(x)\frac{d^{m-1}}{dx^{m-1}} + \cdots + q_m(x)\cdot$$

where $p_i(x) \in C^0$ and $q_j(x) \in C^n$ on some interval I. Then by $\mathbf{LM}$ we mean the linear differential operator $\mathbf{N}$ with the property that

$$\mathbf{N}u = \mathbf{L}(\mathbf{M}u)$$

for any $u \in C^{n+m}(I)$.

To prove (7) we introduce, as before, the notation

$$\mathbf{L}_k = p_{n-k}\frac{d^k}{dx^k}, \qquad 0 \leqq k \leqq n,$$

and

$$\mathbf{M}_j = q_{m-j}\frac{d^j}{dx^j}, \qquad 0 \leqq j \leqq m.$$

Then

$$\mathbf{L} = \sum_{k=0}^{n} \mathbf{L}_k$$

and

$$\mathbf{M} = \sum_{j=0}^{m} \mathbf{M}_j$$

while

$$\mathbf{LM} = \sum_{k=0}^{n}\sum_{j=0}^{m} \mathbf{L}_k\mathbf{M}_j.$$

If we now assume $p_i(x) \in C^{m+n-i}(I)$, $0 \leqq i \leqq n$, and $q_j(x) \in C^{m+n-j}(I)$, $0 \leqq j \leqq m$, then we may form the adjoint of $\mathbf{LM}$. By (1)

$$(\mathbf{LM})^* = \left(\sum_{k,j} \mathbf{L}_k\mathbf{M}_j\right)^* = \sum_{k,j} (\mathbf{L}_k\mathbf{M}_j)^*. \tag{8}$$

Now suppose we can prove that

$$(\mathbf{L}_k\mathbf{M}_j)^* = \mathbf{M}_j^*\mathbf{L}_k^*, \qquad 0 \leqq j \leqq m, \qquad 0 \leqq k \leqq n. \tag{9}$$

Then (8) may be written as

$$\sum_{k,j} (\mathbf{L}_k\mathbf{M}_j)^* = \sum_{k,j} \mathbf{M}_j^*\mathbf{L}_k^* = \left(\sum_{j=0}^{m} \mathbf{M}_j^*\right)\left(\sum_{k=0}^{n} \mathbf{L}_k^*\right) = \mathbf{M}^*\mathbf{L}^*$$

which is (7). Thus we must merely prove (9).

By definition of $\mathbf{L}_k$ and $\mathbf{M}_j$,

$$\mathbf{L}_k\mathbf{M}_j u = p_{n-k}(q_{m-j}u^{(j)})^{(k)}$$
$$= p_{n-k}\sum_{\alpha=0}^{k}\binom{k}{\alpha} q_{m-j}^{(k-\alpha)}\, u^{(j+\alpha)}$$

and

$$(\mathbf{L}_k\mathbf{M}_j)^* u = \sum_{\alpha=0}^{k}\binom{k}{\alpha}(-1)^{j+\alpha}[q_{m-j}^{(k-\alpha)}(p_{n-k}u)]^{(j+\alpha)}$$
$$= \sum_{\alpha=0}^{k}\binom{k}{\alpha}(-1)^{j+\alpha}\{[q_{m-j}^{(k-\alpha)}(p_{n-k}u)]^{(\alpha)}\}^{(j)}$$
$$=(-1)^j\sum_{\alpha=0}^{k}(-1)^{\alpha}\binom{k}{\alpha}\left\{\sum_{\beta=0}^{\alpha}\binom{\alpha}{\beta} q_{m-j}^{(k-\beta)}(p_{n-k}u)^{(\beta)}\right\}^{(j)}$$
$$=(-1)^j\sum_{\alpha=0}^{k}(-1)^{\alpha}\binom{k}{\alpha}\sum_{\beta=0}^{\alpha}\binom{\alpha}{\beta}\sum_{\gamma=0}^{j}\binom{j}{\gamma} q_{m-j}^{(k+j-\beta-\gamma)}(p_{n-k}u)^{(\beta+\gamma)}$$
$$=(-1)^j\sum_{\beta=0}^{k}\left[\sum_{\alpha=\beta}^{k}(-1)^{\alpha}\binom{k}{\alpha}\binom{\alpha}{\beta}\right]\sum_{\gamma=0}^{j}\binom{j}{\gamma} q_{m-j}^{(k+j-\beta-\gamma)}(p_{n-k}u)^{(\beta+\gamma)}.$$

But from (5) and (6), the term in brackets is zero for $\beta \neq k$. Hence

$$(\mathbf{L}_k\mathbf{M}_j)^* u = (-1)^j(-1)^k\binom{k}{k}\binom{k}{k}\sum_{\gamma=0}^{j}\binom{j}{\gamma} q_{m-j}^{(j-\gamma)}(p_{n-k}u)^{(k+\gamma)}$$
$$= (-1)^{j+k}\sum_{\gamma=0}^{j}\binom{j}{\gamma} q_{m-j}^{(j-\gamma)}(p_{n-k}u)^{(k+\gamma)}. \tag{10}$$

But

$$\mathbf{M}_j^*\mathbf{L}_k^* u = (-1)^j[q_{m-j}(-1)^k(p_{n-k}u)^{(k)}]^{(j)}$$
$$= (-1)^{j+k}\sum_{\gamma=0}^{j}\binom{j}{\gamma} q_{m-j}^{(j-\gamma)}(p_{n-k}u)^{(k+\gamma)}$$

which is (10). Thus (9) and hence (7) is established.

To summarize:

Theorem 1. Let $\mathbf{L}$ and $\mathbf{M}$ be linear differential operators of finite order whose coefficients are of class $C^p(I)$ for some p sufficiently large. Then for all x in the interval I,

(i) $(\mathbf{L} + \mathbf{M})^* = \mathbf{L}^* + \mathbf{M}^*$

(ii) $\mathbf{L}^{**} = \mathbf{L}$

(iii) $(\mathbf{LM})^* = \mathbf{M}^*\mathbf{L}^*$.

3. The Adjoint Matrix

We now turn to another interpretation of the adjoint operator. Consider the system of first order differential equations

$$\frac{dY}{dx} = Q(x)\ Y \tag{1}$$

where $Y(x) = \{y_1(x), y_2(x), \cdots, y_n(x)\}$ is a column vector and

$$Q(x) = \| q_{ij}(x) \|_{1 \leqq i, j \leqq n}$$

is a square matrix of functions continuous on some interval I. Then the system

$$\frac{dY^*}{dx} = -Q^*(x)\ Y^*, \tag{2}$$

where Q^* is the *transpose* (sometimes called the *adjoint*) matrix of Q, is called the system *adjoint* to (1). Let us see how this definition compares with the definition of the adjoint operator given in Section 1.

Let

$$\mathbf{L} = p_0(x) \frac{d^n}{dx^n} + p_1(x) \frac{d^{n-1}}{dx^{n-1}} + \cdots + p_n(x)\cdot$$

where $p_i(x) \in C^{n-i}(I)$, $0 \leqq i \leqq n$, and $p_0(x) > 0$ on the same closed interval I. Then by (1.1.5) we may write $\mathbf{L}y = 0$ in the form

$$\frac{dZ}{dx} = P(x)\, Z \tag{3}$$

where

$$P(x) = \left\| \begin{matrix} 0 & 1 & 0 & \cdots & 0 & 0 \\ 0 & 0 & 1 & \cdots & 0 & 0 \\ 0 & 0 & 0 & \cdots & 0 & 0 \\ \cdot & \cdot & \cdot & \cdot & \cdot & \cdot \\ 0 & 0 & 0 & \cdots & 1 & 0 \\ 0 & 0 & 0 & \cdots & 0 & 1 \\ -\frac{p_n}{p_0} & -\frac{p_{n-1}}{p_0} & -\frac{p_{n-2}}{p_0} & \cdots & -\frac{p_2}{p_0} & -\frac{p_1}{p_0} \end{matrix} \right\| . \tag{4}$$

Let $P^*(x)$ be the transpose of $P(x)$, that is, the matrix $P(x)$ with rows and columns interchanged:

$$P^*(x) = \left\| \begin{matrix} 0 & 0 & 0 & \cdots & 0 & 0 & -\frac{p_n}{p_0} \\ 1 & 0 & 0 & \cdots & 0 & 0 & -\frac{p_{n-1}}{p_0} \\ 0 & 1 & 0 & \cdots & 0 & 0 & -\frac{p_{n-2}}{p_0} \\ \cdot & \cdot & \cdot & \cdot & \cdot & \cdot & \cdot \\ 0 & 0 & 0 & \cdots & 1 & 0 & -\frac{p_2}{p_0} \\ 0 & 0 & 0 & \cdots & 0 & 1 & -\frac{p_1}{p_0} \end{matrix} \right\| . \tag{5}$$

Then we may write

$$\frac{dZ^*}{dx} = -P^*(x)\, Z^* \tag{6}$$

where $Z^*(x) = \{z_1^*(x), z_2^*(x), \cdots, z_n^*(x)\}$ is a column vector.

We shall show that if (6) *is reduced to a single* n*th order equation, this equation will be the adjoint* $\mathbf{L}^*z=0$ *of* $\mathbf{L}y=0$ *where* $z = (-1)^n \frac{1}{p_0} z_n^*$.

To prove this assertion we first write (6) in expanded form as:

$$\begin{aligned} \frac{dz_1^*}{dx} &= \frac{p_n}{p_0} z_n^* \\ \frac{dz_2^*}{dx} &= -z_1^* + \frac{p_{n-1}}{p_0} z_n^* \\ \frac{dz_3^*}{dx} &= -z_2^* + \frac{p_{n-2}}{p_0} z_n^* \\ &\cdot \quad \cdot \quad \cdot \quad \cdot \quad \cdot \quad \cdot \quad \cdot \quad \cdot \quad \cdot \\ \frac{dz_k^*}{dx} &= -z_{k-1}^* + \frac{p_{n-k+1}}{p_0} z_n^* \\ &\cdot \quad \cdot \quad \cdot \quad \cdot \quad \cdot \quad \cdot \quad \cdot \quad \cdot \quad \cdot \\ \frac{dz_n^*}{dx} &= -z_{n-1}^* + \frac{p_1}{p_0} z_n^*. \end{aligned} \tag{7}$$

Then

$$\frac{d^2z_n^*}{dx^2} = -\frac{d}{dx}z_{n-1}^* + \frac{d}{dx}\left(\frac{p_1}{p_0}z_n^*\right)$$

$$= z_{n-2}^* - \frac{p_2}{p_0}z_n^* + \frac{d}{dx}\left(\frac{p_1}{p_0}z_n^*\right)$$

and in general

$$\frac{d^nz_n^*}{dx^n} = (-1)^{n-1}\left(\frac{p_n}{p_0}z_n^*\right) + (-1)^{n-2}\frac{d}{dx}\left(\frac{p_{n-1}}{p_0}z_n^*\right)$$

$$+ (-1)^{n-3}\frac{d^2}{dx^2}\left(\frac{p_{n-2}}{p_0}z_n^*\right) + \cdots + (-1)\frac{d^{n-2}}{dx^{n-2}}\left(\frac{p_2}{p_0}z_n^*\right) + \frac{d^{n-1}}{dx^{n-1}}\left(\frac{p_1}{p_0}z_n^*\right).$$

Thus

$$\frac{d^nz_n^*}{dx^n} - \frac{d^{n-1}}{dx^{n-1}}\left(\frac{p_1}{p_0}z_n^*\right) + \cdots + (-1)^{n-1}\frac{d}{dx}\left(\frac{p_{n-1}}{p_0}z_n^*\right) + (-1)^n\left(\frac{p_n}{p_0}z_n^*\right) = 0. \tag{8}$$

Let

$$z_n^* = (-1)^n p_0 z.$$

Then (8) becomes

$$(-1)^n\frac{d^n}{dx^n}(p_0z) + (-1)^{n-1}\frac{d^{n-1}}{dx^{n-1}}(p_1z) + \cdots + (-1)\frac{d}{dx}(p_{n-1}z) + (p_nz) = 0$$

which is precisely $\mathbf{L}^*z = 0$.

3

THE ONE-SIDED GREEN'S FUNCTION

1. The Non-Homogeneous Equation

In Chapter 1 we were concerned with the problem of finding solutions of the *homogeneous* equation

$$\mathbf{L}y = 0$$

where $\mathbf{L}$ was a linear differential operator. Consider now the *non-homogeneous* equation

$$\mathbf{L}y = f(x)$$

where $f(x)$ is not identically zero. Then we ask whether it is possible to find a function $u(x)$ such that $\mathbf{L}u(x) \equiv f(x)$. We shall show in this chapter that it is indeed possible to solve $\mathbf{L}y = f$ in a relatively simple fashion.

Suppose for the moment that such a solution exists. Then it is easy to show that it is unique. For, let

$$\mathbf{L} = p_0(x)\frac{d^n}{dx^n} + p_1(x)\frac{d^{n-1}}{dx^{n-1}} + \cdots + p_n(x)\cdot$$

be a linear differential operator whose coefficients $p_i(x)$, $0 \leqq i \leqq n$, are continuous on some closed finite interval $I = [a,b]$ and $p_0(x) > 0$

on I. Furthermore, let $f(x)$ be continuous on I and suppose $u_1(x)$ has the property that

$$\mathbf{L}u_1(x) \equiv f(x)$$

for all $x \in I$ and

$$u_1^{(i-1)}(x_0) = a_i, \qquad 1 \leqq i \leqq n, \tag{1}$$

at some point x_0 in I. Now suppose $u_2(x)$ also satisfies $\mathbf{L}y = f(x)$ and the initial conditions of (1). Then

$$\delta(x) = u_1(x) - u_2(x)$$

satisfies the homogeneous equation, $\mathbf{L}\delta = 0$, and

$$\delta^{(i-1)}(x_0) = 0, \qquad 1 \leqq i \leqq n.$$

Thus $\delta(x) \equiv 0$ and $u_1(x) \equiv u_2(x)$. That is, if a solution of $\mathbf{L}y = f(x)$ with the initial conditions of (1) exists, then it is unique.

2. Construction of the Green's Function

An elementary technique for solving non-homogeneous equations is the method known as *variation of parameters*. Let us apply it to the simple case where $\mathbf{L}$ is a second order operator. Its generalizations lead to the important concept of *Green's function.*

Let

$$\mathbf{L} = p_0(x)\frac{d^2}{dx^2} + p_1(x)\frac{d}{dx} + p_2(x)\cdot$$

where $p_0(x)$, $p_1(x)$, $p_2(x)$ are continuous on some closed finite interval I and $p_0(x) > 0$ on I. Let $\varphi_1(x)$ and $\varphi_2(x)$ be any two linearly independent solutions of $\mathbf{L}y = 0$. Consider now the equation

$$\mathbf{L}u = f(x)$$

where $f(x)$ is continuous on I. We shall assume that $u(x)$ may be written in the form

$$u(x) = v_1(x)\,\varphi_1(x) + v_2(x)\,\varphi_2(x) \tag{1}$$

where v_1 and v_2 are assumed to be of class $C^1(I)$, but otherwise unspecified. From (1)

$$u'(x) = v_1(x)\varphi_1'(x) + v_2(x)\varphi_2'(x) + [v_1'(x)\varphi_1(x) + v_2'(x)\varphi_2(x)] \tag{2}$$

and as a first condition on the v's we shall require that the term in brackets be zero. Then from (2)

$$u''(x) = v_1(x)\varphi_1''(x) + v_2(x)\varphi_2''(x) + [v_1'(x)\varphi_1'(x) + v_2'(x)\varphi_2'(x)],$$

and as our second condition on the v's we shall require that the term in brackets be equal to $f(x)/p_0(x)$.

If $v_1(x)$ and $v_2(x)$ can be so chosen, then

$$\begin{aligned}\mathbf{L}u &= p_0\left(v_1\varphi_1'' + v_2\varphi_2'' + \frac{f}{p_0}\right) + p_1(v_1\varphi_1' + v_2\varphi_2') + p_2(v_1\varphi_1 + v_2\varphi_2)\\ &= v_1\,\mathbf{L}\varphi_1 + v_2\,\mathbf{L}\varphi_2 + f = f\end{aligned}$$

since $\mathbf{L}\varphi_1 = 0 = \mathbf{L}\varphi_2$. Now the conditions we have imposed on the v's may be written as

$$\begin{aligned} v_1'\,\varphi_1 + v_2'\,\varphi_2 &= 0\\ v_1'\,\varphi_1' + v_2'\,\varphi_2' &= \frac{f}{p_0}.\end{aligned}$$

By Cramer's rule

$$v_1'(x) = -\frac{\varphi_2(x)f(x)}{W(x)p_0(x)}$$

and

$$v_2'(x) = \frac{\varphi_1(x)f(x)}{W(x)p_0(x)}$$

where $W(x) \neq 0$ is the Wronskian of $\varphi_1(x)$ and $\varphi_2(x)$. Hence

$$v_1(x) = -\int_{x_0}^{x} \frac{\varphi_2(\xi)f(\xi)}{p_0(\xi)W(\xi)}\,d\xi + c_1 \tag{3}$$

and

$$v_2(x) = \int_{x_0}^{x} \frac{\varphi_1(\xi)f(\xi)}{p_0(\xi)W(\xi)}\,d\xi + c_2 \tag{4}$$

where c_1 and c_2 are constants of integration and x and x_0 are in I. If we substitute (3) and (4) in (1), then

$$u(x) = c_1\varphi_1(x) + c_2\varphi_2(x) - \int_{x_0}^{x} \frac{[\varphi_1(x)\varphi_2(\xi) - \varphi_2(x)\varphi_1(\xi)]}{p_0(\xi)W(\xi)}\,f(\xi)\,d\xi. \tag{5}$$

Thus if we let

$$H(x, \xi) = -\frac{1}{p_0(\xi)} \frac{\begin{vmatrix} \varphi_1(x) & \varphi_2(x) \\ \varphi_1(\xi) & \varphi_2(\xi) \end{vmatrix}}{\begin{vmatrix} \varphi_1(\xi) & \varphi_2(\xi) \\ \varphi_1'(\xi) & \varphi_2'(\xi) \end{vmatrix}}, \tag{6}$$

equation (5) may be written as

$$u(x) = c_1\varphi_1(x) + c_2\varphi_2(x) + \int_{x_0}^{x} H(x, \xi) f(\xi)\, d\xi.$$

We call $H(x, \xi)$ as defined by (6) the *one-sided Green's function* for the second-order linear differential operator $\mathbf{L}$. We readily see that

$$\psi(x) = \int_{x_0}^{x} H(x, \xi)\, f(\xi)\, d\xi$$

is a solution of $\mathbf{L}y = f$ with the property that

$$\psi(x_0) = 0 = \psi'(x_0).$$

We shall write symbolically

$$\psi(x) = \mathbf{L}^{-1}f(x)$$

and call $\mathbf{L}^{-1}$ the *inverse operator* to $\mathbf{L}$. Clearly

$$\mathbf{L}\,\psi(x) = f(x) = \mathbf{L}(\mathbf{L}^{-1}f(x))$$

and

$$\mathbf{L}\mathbf{L}^{-1} = \mathbf{I}$$

where $\mathbf{I}$ is the identity operator. Also

$$\mathbf{L}^{-1}\mathbf{L} = \mathbf{I},$$

since

$$\mathbf{L}^{-1}\mathbf{L}\psi = \mathbf{L}^{-1}f = \psi.$$

We now turn to the definition of the Green's function for nth order linear differential equations.

Definition. Let

$$\mathbf{L} = p_0(x)\frac{d^n}{dx^n} + p_1(x)\frac{d^{n-1}}{dx^{n-1}} + \cdots + p_n(x)\cdot$$

be a linear differential operator of the nth order where $p_i(x) \in C^0(I)$, $0 \leqq i \leqq n$, and $p_0(x) > 0$ on I where I is a closed finite interval. Let $\{\varphi_j(x) \mid 1 \leqq j \leqq n\}$ be a fundamental set of solutions of $\mathbf{L}y = 0$. Then

$$H(x,\xi) = \frac{(-1)^{n-1}}{p_0(\xi)W(\xi)} \begin{vmatrix} \varphi_1(x) & \varphi_2(x) & \cdots & \varphi_n(x) \\ \varphi_1(\xi) & \varphi_2(\xi) & \cdots & \varphi_n(\xi) \\ \varphi_1'(\xi) & \varphi_2'(\xi) & \cdots & \varphi_n'(\xi) \\ \cdot & \cdot & \cdot & \cdot \\ \varphi_1^{(n-2)}(\xi) & \varphi_2^{(n-2)}(\xi) & \cdots & \varphi_n^{(n-2)}(\xi) \end{vmatrix}, \quad (7)$$

where $W(\xi)$ is the Wronskian of the $\varphi_j(\xi)$, is called the *one-sided Green's function* for $\mathbf{L}$.

As an immediate consequence of this definition we see that the Green's function enjoys the following properties:

Theorem 1. Let $H(x,\xi)$ be the one-sided Green's function for the nth order linear differential operator $\mathbf{L}$. Then

(i) $H(x,\xi)$ and $\frac{\partial^k}{\partial x^k} H(x,\xi)$, $1 \leqq k \leqq n$, are jointly continuous in x and ξ on the square $I \times I$.

(ii) $\left.\frac{\partial^k}{\partial x^k} H(x,\xi)\right|_{x=\xi} = 0 \quad \text{for} \quad 0 \leqq k \leqq n-2$

(iii) $\left.\frac{\partial^{n-1}}{\partial x^{n-1}} H(x,\xi)\right|_{x=\xi} = \frac{1}{p_0(\xi)}$

(iv) $\mathbf{L}_x H(x,\xi) = 0$, where the subscript x on $\mathbf{L}$ indicates that $\mathbf{L}$ is to operate on the variable x.

We shall leave the proof of these elementary properties to the reader.

The main result of this section is expressed in the following theorem:

Theorem 2. Let

$$\mathbf{L} = p_0(x)\frac{d^n}{dx^n} + p_1(x)\frac{d^{n-1}}{dx^{n-1}} + \cdots + p_n(x)\cdot$$

be a linear differential operator where the $p_i(x) \in C^0(I)$, $0 \leqq i \leqq n$, and $p_0(x) > 0$ on I where I is a closed finite interval. Let $\varphi_j(x)$, $1 \leqq j \leqq n$, be a fundamental set of solutions of $\mathbf{L}y=0$. Let $W(x)$ be the Wronskian of the $\varphi_j(x)$ and $H(x,\xi)$ the one-sided Green's function for $\mathbf{L}$. Let $f(x)$ be any function continuous on I and x_0 any point in I. Then for all $x \in I$,

$$u(x) = \int_{x_0}^{x} H(x,\xi)\, f(\xi)\, d\xi \tag{8}$$

is a solution of the non-homogeneous equation

$$\mathbf{L}y = f(x)$$

which satisfies the boundary conditions

$$u^{(k)}(x_0) = 0, \qquad 0 \leqq k \leqq n-1.$$

Proof. For convenience in notation set $H_j(x,\xi)$ equal to

$$\frac{\partial^j H(x,\xi)}{\partial x^j}$$

for $0 \leqq j \leqq n$. Then from (8),

$$u'(x) = H(x,x)\, f(x) + \int_{x_0}^{x} H_1(x,\xi) f(\xi)\, d\xi$$

$$= \int_{x_0}^{x} H_1(x,\xi)\, f(\xi)\, d\xi$$

since $H(x,x)=0$ by (ii) of Theorem 1. Similarly

$$u^{(k)}(x) = \int_{x_0}^{x} H_k(x,\xi)\, f(\xi)\, d\xi, \qquad 0 \leqq k \leqq n-1, \tag{9}$$

and

$$u^{(n)}(x) = H_{n-1}(x,x)\, f(x) + \int_{x_0}^{x} H_n(x,\xi)\, f(\xi)\, d\xi$$

$$= \frac{f(x)}{p_0(x)} + \int_{x_0}^{x} H_n(x,\xi)\, f(\xi)\, d\xi$$

by (iii) of Theorem 1. If we multiply $u^{(k)}(x)$ by $p_{n-k}(x)$ and sum over k, $0 \leqq k \leqq n$, we obtain

$$\mathbf{L}u(x) = f(x) + \int_{x_0}^{x} \mathbf{L}_x H(x,\xi)\, f(\xi)\, d\xi = f(x)$$

by virtue of (iv) of Theorem 1. Hence we have shown that $\mathbf{L}u = f$.

From (9),

$$u^{(k)}(x_0) = 0, \qquad 0 \leqq k \leqq n-1,$$

which establishes our conclusion regarding the initial values of u and its first $n-1$ derivatives.

The uniqueness of the Green's function is proved in the next theorem.

Theorem 3. Let $H(x,\xi)$ be as defined by (7). Let $K(x,\xi)$ be any function jointly continuous on $I \times I$ with the property that

$$u(x) = \int_{x_0}^{x} K(x,\xi)\, f(\xi)\, d\xi$$

is a solution of the non-homogeneous equation $\mathbf{L}y = f$ for every $f(x)$ continuous on I, and assumes the initial values $u^{(k)}(x_0) = 0, 0 \leqq k \leqq n-1$. Then $K(x,\xi) \equiv H(x,\xi)$ on $I \times I$.

Proof. By Theorem 2

$$u(x) = \int_{x_0}^{x} H(x,\xi)\, f(\xi)\, d\xi$$

and by hypothesis

$$u(x) = \int_{x_0}^{x} K(x,\xi)\, f(\xi)\, d\xi.$$

Thus

$$\int_{x_0}^{x} [H(x,\xi) - K(x,\xi)]\, f(\xi)\, d\xi \equiv 0 \tag{10}$$

for all $x \in I$. Let $J(x,\xi) = H(x,\xi) - K(x,\xi)$. Then $J(x,\xi)$ is jointly continuous on $I \times I$. Suppose J is not identically zero. Then there exists a point (x',ξ') in $I \times I$ such that

$$J(x',\xi') \neq 0.$$

By the continuity of J there exists a $\delta > 0$ and a neighborhood $N = \{|x - x'| < \delta,\ |\xi - \xi'| < \delta\}$ such that $J(x,\xi) \neq 0$ for $(x,\xi) \in N$. (We leave to the reader the obvious modifications when x' and/or ξ' is an endpoint of I.) If $x_0 \leqq \xi'$, choose an $f(x)$, continuous on I, such that $f(x) \neq 0$ in the interval $(\xi', \xi' + \delta)$ and is zero elsewhere in I. Then there is an $x \in I$ such that

$$\int_{x_0}^{x} J(x',\xi) f(\xi)\, d\xi = \int_{\xi'}^{\xi'+\delta} J(x',\xi) f(\xi)\, d\xi \neq 0$$

which contradicts (10). If $x_0 > \xi'$, choose an $f(x)$, continuous on I, such that $f(x) \neq 0$ in the interval $(\xi' - \delta,\ \xi)$ and is zero elsewhere in I.

3. Green's Function of the Adjoint Operator

From (2.7) we see that the Green's function $H(x,\xi)$ may be written in the form

$$H(x,\xi) = \sum_{i=1}^{n} \varphi_i(x)\ \varphi_i^*(\xi) \tag{1}$$

where

$$\varphi_i^*(\xi) = \frac{1}{p_0(\xi) W(\xi)} \frac{\partial\ W(\xi)}{\partial \varphi_i^{(n-1)}(\xi)} = \frac{1}{p_0(\xi)} \frac{\partial \log W}{\partial \varphi_i^{(n-1)}},\ 1 \leqq i \leqq n, \tag{2}$$

$W(x)$ being the Wronskian of the $\varphi_j(x)$.

We shall now show that the $\varphi_i^*(x)$, $1 \leqq i \leqq n$, defined by (2) form a fundamental system of solutions for the *adjoint operator* $\mathbf{L}^*$. Preliminary to this proof we shall show that $H(x,\xi) = -H^*(\xi,x)$ where H^* is the Green's function for $\mathbf{L}^*$. The proof of this formula uses Green's formula.

Theorem 4. Let

$$\mathbf{L} = p_0(x) \frac{d^n}{dx^n} + p_1(x) \frac{d^{n-1}}{dx^{n-1}} + \cdots + p_n(x).$$

where $p_i(x) \in C^{n-i}(I)$, $0 \leqq i \leqq n$, and $p_0(x) > 0$ on some closed finite interval I. Let $\mathbf{L}^*$ be the adjoint of $\mathbf{L}$ and $H(x,\xi)$ the one-sided Green's function for $\mathbf{L}$. Let $H^*(x,\xi)$ be the one-sided Green's function for $\mathbf{L}^*$. Then

$$H^*(\xi,x) = -H(x,\xi).$$

Proof. By Green's formula

$$\int_\xi^\zeta [H^*(x,\zeta)\,\mathbf{L}_x H(x,\xi) - H(x,\xi)\,\mathbf{L}_x^*\, H^*(x,\zeta)]\,dx = \pi_x[H(x,\xi),\, H^*(x,\zeta)]\Big|_\xi^\zeta \tag{3}$$

where π is the Lagrange bilinear concomitant and the subscript x on π indicates that we are to operate on the variable x. We may write $\pi[u,v]$ in the form

$$\pi[u,v] = (vp_0)u^{(n-1)} + (-1)^{n-1}(vp_0)^{(n-1)}u + \sigma[u,v] \tag{4}$$

where $\sigma[u,v]$ is a linear combination of terms of the form $u^{(j)}v^{(k)}$ with $0 \leqq j,\, k \leqq n-2$.

By (ii) of Theorem 1, $\sigma_x[H(x,\xi),\, H^*(x,\zeta)]$ vanishes at $x=\xi$ and $x=\zeta$. Also by (iv) of Theorem 1, $\mathbf{L}_x H(x,\xi)=0=\mathbf{L}_x^* H^*(x,\zeta)$. Then (3) and (4) imply that

$$0=\left\{[H^*(x,\zeta)p_0(x)]\,\frac{\partial^{n-1}}{\partial x^{n-1}}H(x,\xi)+(-1)^{n-1}\left[\frac{\partial^{n-1}}{\partial x^{n-1}}H^*(x,\zeta)p_0(x)\right]H(x,\xi)\right\}\Bigg|_\xi^\zeta$$

or

$$0 = -H^*(\xi,\zeta)p_0(\xi)\frac{1}{p_0(\xi)} + (-1)^{n-1}\left[\frac{(-1)^n}{p_0(\zeta)}p_0(\zeta)\right] H(\zeta,\xi).$$

Thus

$$H^*(\xi,\zeta) = -H(\zeta,\xi)$$

for any two values ξ and ζ in I.

An immediate corollary of this theorem is:

Corollary. If $H(x,\xi) = \sum_{i=1}^n \varphi_i(x)\varphi_i^*(\xi)$ is the one-sided Green's function for $\mathbf{L}$, then the $\varphi_i^*(x)$, $1 \leqq i \leqq n$, are solutions of the adjoint equation $\mathbf{L}^*z=0$.

We shall now show that the $\varphi_i^*(x)$ form a fundamental system of solutions of $\mathbf{L}^*z=0$.

Theorem 5. Let

$$\mathbf{L} = p_0(x)\frac{d^n}{dx^n} + p_1(x)\frac{d^{n-1}}{dx^{n-1}} + \cdots + p_n(x)\cdot$$

where $p_i(x) \in C^{n-i}(I)$, $0 \leqq i \leqq n$, and $p_0(x)>0$ on some closed finite interval I. Let $\mathbf{L}^*$ be the adjoint of $\mathbf{L}$ and $H(x,\xi)$ the one-sided Green's function of $\mathbf{L}$. Let

$$H(x,\xi) = \sum_{i=1}^{n} \varphi_i(x)\, \varphi_i^*(\xi).$$

Then the $\varphi_i^*(x)$, $1 \leqq i \leqq n$, form a fundamental set of solutions of $\mathbf{L}^*z=0$.

Proof. Let $\psi^*(x)$ be any solution of $\mathbf{L}^*z=0$. Then by Green's formula

$$0 = \int_{\xi_0}^{\xi} [\psi^*(x)\,\mathbf{L}_x H(x,\xi) - H(x,\xi)\,\mathbf{L}_x^*\psi^*(x)]\,dx$$

$$= \pi_x[H(x,\xi),\, \psi^*(x)]\Big|_{\xi_0}^{\xi}.$$

But at $x=\xi$

$$\pi_x[H(\xi,\xi),\, \psi^*(\xi)] = \psi^*(\xi).$$

Thus

$$\psi^*(\xi) = \pi_x[H(\xi_0,\xi),\, \psi^*(\xi_0)].$$

That is, $\psi^*(\xi)$ is a linear combination, with constant coefficients, of the $\varphi_i^*(\xi)$, $1 \leqq i \leqq n$. By Theorem 6 of Chapter 1, the $\varphi_i^*(x)$, $1 \leqq i \leqq n$, form a fundamental set of solutions of $\mathbf{L}^*z=0$.

4. Further Properties of the Green's Function

If we have a fundamental system of solutions of $\mathbf{L}y=0$, then we have seen that the Green's function $H(x,\xi)$ may be constructed explicitly. The converse is also true. That is, given $H(x,\xi)$ we may construct a fundamental set of solutions of $\mathbf{L}y=0$. We prove this contention in Theorem 6 below.

Theorem 6. Let

$$\mathbf{L} = p_0(x)\frac{d^n}{dx^n} + p_1(x)\frac{d^{n-1}}{dx^{n-1}} + \cdots + p_n(x)\cdot$$

be a linear differential operator where $p_i(x) \in C^{n-i}$, $0 \leqq i \leqq n$, and $p_0(x) > 0$ on some closed finite interval I. Let $H(x,\xi)$ be the one-sided Green's function for $\mathbf{L}$. Then for any $x_0 \in I$,

$$\psi_{k+1}(x) = \frac{\partial^k}{\partial\xi^k} H(x,x_0), \qquad 0 \leqq k \leqq n-1,$$

form a fundamental set of solutions of $\mathbf{L}y=0$.

Proof. By (3.1) the $\psi_k(x)$ are solutions of $\mathbf{L}y=0$. Also from (3.1) we may write

$$H(x,\xi) = \sum_{i=1}^{n} \varphi_i(x)\, \varphi_i^*(\xi)$$

where $\{\varphi_i(x) \mid 1 \leqq i \leqq n\}$ is a fundamental set of solutions of $\mathbf{L}y=0$ and by Theorem 5 the $\varphi_i^*(x)$, $1 \leqq i \leqq n$, form a fundamental system for $\mathbf{L}^*z=0$. Now

$$\psi_{k+1}(x) = \frac{\partial^k}{\partial\xi^k} H(x,x_0) = \sum_{i=1}^{n} \varphi_i(x)\, \varphi_i^{*(k)}(x_0). \tag{1}$$

Hence

$$W_\psi(x) = W_\varphi(x)\, W_{\varphi^*}(x_0)$$

where W_ψ, W_φ, and W_{φ^*} are the Wronskians of the ψ_k, φ_i, and φ_i^* respectively. Since the φ_i and φ_i^* are fundamental systems, $W_\varphi(x) \neq 0 \neq W_{\varphi^*}(x)$ on I, and we have $W_\psi(x) \neq 0$ on I. Thus $\{\psi_k(x) \mid 1 \leqq k \leqq n\}$ is a fundamental set of solutions for $\mathbf{L}y=0$.

Theorem 6 and the definition of the Green's function establish the equivalence of a fundamental system and the Green's function. For if $\{\varphi_j(x) \mid 1 \leqq j \leqq n\}$ is a fundamental system for $\mathbf{L}y=0$, then by definition of the Green's function we may construct $H(x,\xi)$. Conversely, by Theorem 6, given $H(x,\xi)$ we may construct a fundamental system of solutions of $\mathbf{L}y=0$.

It is also possible to compute the Wronskian in a simple fashion from the Green's function. From Theorem 1,

$$H_{n-1}(\xi,\xi) = \frac{1}{p_0(\xi)} \tag{2}$$

and

$$H_n(\xi,\xi) = -\frac{p_1(\xi)}{p_0^2(\xi)} \tag{3}$$

where we are again using the notation

$$H_k(x,\xi) = \frac{\partial^k}{\partial x^k} H(x,\xi), \qquad 0 \leqq k \leqq n.$$

Thus

$$\frac{H_n(\xi,\xi)}{H_{n-1}(\xi,\xi)} = -\frac{p_1(\xi)}{p_0(\xi)}. \tag{4}$$

But

$$p_0(x)\, W'(x) + p_1(x)\, W(x) = 0.$$

Hence

$$H_{n-1}(x,x)\, W'(x) - H_n(x,x)\, W(x) = 0$$

and

$$W(x) = W(x_0)\, e^{-\int_{x_0}^{x} k(\xi)\, d\xi} \tag{5}$$

where

$$k(\xi) = -\frac{H_n(\xi,\xi)}{H_{n-1}(\xi,\xi)}.$$

In Section 2 of Chapter 2 the composition **LM** of two linear differential operators was defined. We shall now prove the important result that the Green's function of **LM** is the convolution of the Green's functions of **L** and **M**. Precisely:

Theorem 7. Let

$$\mathbf{L} = p_0(x)\frac{d^n}{dx^n} + p_1(x)\frac{d^{n-1}}{dx^{n-1}} + \cdots + p_n(x).$$

and

$$\mathbf{M} = q_0(x)\frac{d^m}{dx^m} + q_1(x)\frac{d^{m-1}}{dx^{m-1}} + \cdots + q_m(x)\cdot$$

be linear differential operators where $p_i(x) \in C^0$ and $q_j(x) \in C^n$ on some closed finite interval I and $p_0(x) > 0$, $q_0(x) > 0$ on I. Let $H_L(x,\xi)$, $H_M(x,\xi)$, and $H_{LM}(x,\xi)$ be the one-sided Green's functions of $\mathbf{L}$, $\mathbf{M}$, and $\mathbf{LM}$ respectively. Then

$$H_{LM}(x,\xi) = \int_\xi^x H_M(x,\zeta)\, H_L(\zeta,\xi)\, d\zeta. \tag{6}$$

Proof. Let $v(x)$ be any function continuous on I. Define $w(x)$ and $u(x)$ by

$$w(\zeta) = \int_{x_0}^{\zeta} H_L(\zeta,\xi)\, v(\xi)\, d\xi \tag{7}$$

and

$$u(x) = \int_{x_0}^{x} H_M(x,\zeta)\, w(\zeta)\, d\zeta \tag{8}$$

respectively for some $x_0 \in I$. Then

$$\mathbf{L}w = v$$

and

$$\mathbf{M}u = w.$$

Hence

$$\mathbf{LM}u = \mathbf{L}w = v.$$

Since $u^{(k)}(x_0) = 0,\ 0 \leqq k \leqq n + m - 1$,

$$u(x) = \int_{x_0}^{x} H_{LM}(x,\xi)\, v(\xi)\, d\xi. \tag{9}$$

Substitute (7) in (8) to obtain

$$u(x) = \int_{x_0}^{x} H_M(x,\zeta) \left[\int_{x_0}^{\zeta} H_L(\zeta,\xi)\, v(\xi)\, d\xi \right] d\zeta.$$

If we interchange the order of integration,

$$u(x) = \int_{x_0}^{x} \left[\int_{\xi}^{x} H_M(x,\zeta)\, H_L(\zeta,\xi)\, d\zeta \right] v(\xi)\, d\xi.$$

A comparison of this formula with (9) and the uniqueness of the Green's function establish the theorem.

4

THE ALGEBRA OF DIFFERENTIAL OPERATORS

1. Rings of Operators

In Section 2 of Chapter 2 we proved that the adjoint operator enjoyed certain algebraic properties. We wish to continue our discussion of the algebra of linear differential operators and the associated bilinear form. Consider, then, the set $\mathscr{L}_0$ of all linear differential operators of finite order whose coefficients are continuous on some interval I. If $\mathbf{L}$ and $\mathbf{M}$ belong to $\mathscr{L}_0$, then it is easy to see that $\mathbf{L} + \mathbf{M}$ is also a member of $\mathscr{L}_0$. Associativity of addition of linear differential operators follows immediately from the corresponding property for real continuous functions. Also, the linear differential operator $\mathbf{0}$ which is identically zero on I is in $\mathscr{L}_0$ and $\mathbf{L} + \mathbf{0} = \mathbf{0} + \mathbf{L} = \mathbf{L}$ for $\mathbf{L} \in \mathscr{L}_0$. Finally, if

$$\mathbf{L} = p_0 \frac{d^n}{dx^n} + p_1 \frac{d^{n-1}}{dx^{n-1}} + \cdots + p_n \cdot$$

is in $\mathscr{L}_0$, then so is

$$-\mathbf{L} = (-p_0) \frac{d^n}{dx^n} + (-p_1) \frac{d^{n-1}}{dx^{n-1}} + \cdots + (-p_n) \cdot$$

and

$$\mathbf{L} + (-\mathbf{L}) = -\mathbf{L} + \mathbf{L} = \mathbf{0}.$$

Thus we see that $\mathscr{L}_0$ is an additive group. Furthermore, since $\mathbf{L} + \mathbf{M} = \mathbf{M} + \mathbf{L}$ for $\mathbf{L}$ and $\mathbf{M}$ in $\mathscr{L}_0$, it follows that $\mathscr{L}_0$ is abelian.

The additive group properties of $\mathscr{L}_0$ were deduced without explicit reference to the class of functions upon which the members of $\mathscr{L}_0$ were to operate. It is necessary to mention such admissible functions when discussing the multiplicative properties of linear differential operators. We recall in Section 2 of Chapter 2 that we defined the composition $\mathbf{LM}$ of two linear differential operators $\mathbf{L}$ and $\mathbf{M}$. Thus if† $\partial\mathbf{L} = n$, $\partial\mathbf{M} = m$, and $u \in C^{n+m}$ on some interval I, then by $\mathbf{LM}$ we meant the linear differential operator $\mathbf{N}$ with the property that

$$\mathbf{N}u = \mathbf{L}(\mathbf{M}u).$$

Since we are operating on the *coefficients* of $\mathbf{M}$ as well as on the function u, we must require that these coefficients belong to $C^n(I)$. Thus if $\mathbf{L}$ and $\mathbf{M}$ belong to $\mathscr{L}_0$, $\mathbf{LM}$ need not be defined. We overcome this difficulty by considering the class $\mathscr{L}$ of linear differential operators whose coefficients are of class‡ C^∞ on some interval I. Since $\mathscr{L}$ is additively closed, it follows from the properties of $\mathscr{L}_0$ that $\mathscr{L}$ is an additive abelian group.

Thus we see that if $\mathbf{L}, \mathbf{M} \in \mathscr{L}$, then $\mathbf{LM} \in \mathscr{L}$ and $\mathscr{L}$ is multiplicatively closed. We shall prove the associativity below. That is, if $\mathbf{L}$, $\mathbf{M}$, $\mathbf{N}$ are linear differential operators of class $\mathscr{L}$, then

$$\mathbf{L}(\mathbf{MN}) = (\mathbf{LM})\mathbf{N}. \tag{1}$$

Right and left distributivity, viz.:

$$(\mathbf{M} + \mathbf{N})\mathbf{L} = \mathbf{ML} + \mathbf{NL}$$

and

$$\mathbf{L}(\mathbf{M} + \mathbf{N}) = \mathbf{LM} + \mathbf{LN}$$

is readily verified for members of $\mathscr{L}$. Assuming (1) is valid for the moment, we see that $\mathscr{L}$ is a ring. Furthermore, if $\mathbf{I}$ $(=1)$ is the identity operator, $\mathbf{LI} = \mathbf{IL} = \mathbf{L}$. Thus $\mathscr{L}$ has a unity element. However,

† If $\mathbf{L}$ is a linear differential operator we shall frequently use the notation $\partial\mathbf{L}$ to indicate the *order* of $\mathbf{L}$, that is, the order of the highest derivative appearing in $\mathbf{L}$ with non-identically zero coefficient.

‡ By $C^\infty(I)$ we mean the class of all functions continuous on I which have continuous derivatives of all orders. That is, $C^\infty(I)$ is the intersection of the classes $C^k(I)$ for all $k > 0$,

$$C^\infty(I) = \bigcap_{k \geqq 1} C^k(I).$$

$\mathscr{L}$ is not commutative as can be verified by simple example. Formalizing, we have the following theorem:

Theorem 1. Let $\mathscr{L}$ be the totality of linear differential operators of finite order whose coefficients are of class C^∞ on some interval I. Then under the binary operations of addition and multiplication, $\mathscr{L}$ is a ring with a unity element.

It remains but to prove the associative law of (1) in order to establish Theorem 1 completely. Let $f(x)$, $g(x)$, $h(x)$ be of class $C^\infty(I)$, and let

$$\begin{aligned} \mathbf{L} &= f(x)\frac{d^n}{dx^n} \\ \mathbf{M} &= g(x)\frac{d^m}{dx^m} \\ \mathbf{N} &= h(x)\frac{d^p}{dx^p}. \end{aligned} \tag{2}$$

It is easy to see that if we can prove (1) for the particular operators **L**, **M**, and **N** of (2), then the associativity will be established in the general case.

Now let $u \in C^\infty(I)$. Then

$$(\mathbf{MN})u = g(hu^{(p)})^{(m)} = g\sum_{\alpha=0}^{m}\binom{m}{\alpha} h^{(m-\alpha)}\, u^{(p+\alpha)}$$

and

$$\begin{aligned} \mathbf{L}(\mathbf{MN})u &= f\sum_{\alpha=0}^{m}\binom{m}{\alpha}[gh^{(m-\alpha)}\, u^{(p+\alpha)}]^{(n)} \\ &= f\sum_{\alpha=0}^{m}\binom{m}{\alpha}\sum_{\beta=0}^{n}\binom{n}{\beta} g^{(n-\beta)}\,[h^{(m-\alpha)}\, u^{(p+\alpha)}]^{(\beta)} \\ &= f\sum_{\alpha=0}^{m}\sum_{\beta=0}^{n}\binom{m}{\alpha}\binom{n}{\beta} g^{(n-\beta)}\sum_{\gamma=0}^{\beta}\binom{\beta}{\gamma} h^{(m-\alpha+\beta-\gamma)}\, u^{(p+\alpha+\gamma)}. \end{aligned} \tag{3}$$

On the other hand, for $v \in C^\infty(I)$,

$$(\mathbf{LM})v = f[gv^{(m)}]^{(n)} = f\sum_{\beta=0}^{n}\binom{n}{\beta} g^{(n-\beta)}\, v^{(m+\beta)}$$

and

$$
\begin{aligned}
(\mathbf{LM})\mathbf{N}u &= f\sum_{\beta=0}^{n}\binom{n}{\beta} g^{(n-\beta)}\,[hu^{(p)}]^{(m+\beta)} \\
&= f\sum_{\beta=0}^{n}\binom{n}{\beta} g^{(n-\beta)}[(hu^{(p)})^{(\beta)}]^{(m)} \\
&= f\sum_{\beta=0}^{n}\binom{n}{\beta} g^{(n-\beta)}\left[\sum_{\gamma=0}^{\beta}\binom{\beta}{\gamma} h^{(\beta-\gamma)}\,u^{(p+\gamma)}\right]^{(m)} \\
&= f\sum_{\beta=0}^{n}\binom{n}{\beta} g^{(n-\beta)}\sum_{\gamma=0}^{\beta}\binom{\beta}{\gamma}\sum_{\alpha=0}^{m}\binom{m}{\alpha} h^{(\beta-\gamma+m-\alpha)}\,u^{(p+\gamma+\alpha)}
\end{aligned}
$$

which is identical with (3).

2. Inverses of Differential Operators

In establishing Theorem 1 we had no need to mention the multiplicative inverses of linear differential operators. However, if $\mathbf{L}$ is a linear differential operator we have, in certain instances, computed its inverse $\mathbf{L}^{-1}$ in terms of the one-sided Green's function (cf. Section 2 of Chapter 3). Thus if I is a closed interval and $\mathbf{L} \in \mathscr{L}$ has the property that its leading coefficient does not vanish on I, then for any $v(x) \in C^{\infty}(I)$ we can find a $u(x)$ such that

$$\mathbf{L}u = v.$$

Precisely, if $H(x,\xi)$ is the one-sided Green's function for $\mathbf{L}$, then

$$u(x) = \int_{x_0}^{x} H(x,\xi)\, v(\xi)\, d\xi \tag{1}$$

where x_0 is any point in I. Clearly $u(x)$ is also of class $C^{\infty}(I)$ and has the property that

$$u^{(k-1)}(x_0) = 0, \qquad 1 \leqq k \leqq \partial\mathbf{L}.$$

We shall write (1) symbolically as

$$u = \mathbf{L}^{-1} v. \tag{2}$$

From (2),

$$\mathbf{L}u = \mathbf{L}(\mathbf{L}^{-1}v) = \mathbf{I}v = v$$

as we showed in Theorem 2 of Chapter 3. If u is given and

$$\mathbf{L}u = v, \tag{3}$$

then it does not follow that

$$u = \mathbf{L}^{-1}v$$

unless u is so chosen that $u^{(k-1)}(x_0)=0$, $1 \leqq k \leqq \partial\mathbf{L}$. If $u^{(k-1)}(x_0)=a_k$, $1 \leqq k \leqq \partial\mathbf{L}$, then the inverse of (3) must be written

$$\begin{aligned} u(x) &= \int_{x_0}^{x} H(x,\xi)\, v(\xi)\, d\xi + \Delta(x) \\ &= \mathbf{L}^{-1}v + \Delta(x) \end{aligned} \tag{4}$$

where $\Delta(x)$ is a linear combination of a fundamental set of solutions of $\mathbf{L}y=0$ so chosen that

$$\Delta^{(k-1)}(x_0) = a_k, \qquad 1 \leqq k \leqq \partial\mathbf{L}.$$

Summarizing and slightly generalizing our conclusions, we may state:

Theorem 2. Let $\mathbf{L}$ be a linear differential operator of order n whose coefficients are continuous on some closed finite interval I and whose leading coefficient does not vanish on I. Then

(i) $\mathbf{L}\mathbf{L}^{-1}u = u$ for all $u \in C^0(I)$

(ii) $\mathbf{L}^{-1}\mathbf{L}u = u$ for all $u \in C^n(I)$ such that $u^{(k-1)}(x_0)=0$, $1 \leqq k \leqq n$, for some point $x_0 \in I$.

Let us now consider the inverse of the composition $\mathbf{LM}$ of two linear differential operators. In Theorem 7 of Chapter 3 we showed how to construct explicitly the one-sided Green's function for $\mathbf{LM}$ in terms of the Green's functions of $\mathbf{L}$ and $\mathbf{M}$. Here we shall establish the validity of the symbolic equation

$$(\mathbf{LM})^{-1} = \mathbf{M}^{-1}\mathbf{L}^{-1}.$$

Let $\mathbf{L}$ and $\mathbf{M}$ be of orders n and m respectively and let their coefficients be of class C^∞ on some closed finite interval I. Furthermore, let the leading coefficients of $\mathbf{L}$ and $\mathbf{M}$ be non-vanishing on I. Let $v(x)$ be any function continuous on I and define $w(x)$ and $u(x)$ by the equations

$$w = \mathbf{L}^{-1}v \tag{5}$$

and

$$u = \mathbf{M}^{-1}w \tag{6}$$

respectively. Of course $\mathbf{L}^{-1}$ and $\mathbf{M}^{-1}$ are to be interpreted in terms of the one-sided Green's functions of $\mathbf{L}$ and $\mathbf{M}$ respectively with respect to some fixed point x_0 in I. From (5) we conclude that $w^{(k)}(x_0) = 0$, $0 \leqq k \leqq n - 1$. This fact and (6) imply

$$u^{(k)}(x_0) = 0, \qquad 0 \leqq k \leqq n + m - 1. \tag{7}$$

Equations (6) and (5) may be combined to write

$$u = \mathbf{M}^{-1}(\mathbf{L}^{-1}v) = (\mathbf{M}^{-1}\mathbf{L}^{-1})v. \tag{8}$$

But from (5) and (6) follows $v = \mathbf{L}w$ and $w = \mathbf{M}u$ respectively. Thus

$$(\mathbf{LM})u = \mathbf{L}(\mathbf{M}u) = \mathbf{L}w = v$$

and by virtue of (7)

$$u = (\mathbf{LM})^{-1}v. \tag{9}$$

Equations (8) and (9) then imply

$$\mathbf{M}^{-1}\mathbf{L}^{-1} = (\mathbf{LM})^{-1} \tag{10}$$

as we wished to prove.

We now turn to the problem of considering the composition of a linear differential operator with an inverse operator. In particular we wish to establish the symbolic formula

$$(\mathbf{ML}^{-1})^{-1} = \mathbf{LM}^{-1}.$$

Let $\partial\mathbf{L} = n$, $\partial\mathbf{M} = m$, and let the coefficients of $\mathbf{L}$ and $\mathbf{M}$ be of class C^∞ on some closed finite interval I. Let the leading coefficients of $\mathbf{L}$ and $\mathbf{M}$ be non-vanishing on I.

Now let $u(x)$ be any function of class $C^n(I)$ such that $u^{(k-1)}(x_0) = 0$, $1 \leqq k \leqq n$, for some point x_0 in I, and define $w(x)$ by the equation

$$w = \mathbf{M}^{-1}u. \tag{11}$$

Then $w(x) \in C^{m+n}(I)$ and $w^{(k-1)}(x_0) = 0$, $1 \leqq k \leqq m + n$. Define $v(x)$ by the equation

$$\mathbf{L}w = v. \tag{12}$$

Then $v(x) \in C^m(I)$. From (12) and (11)

$$v = \mathbf{L}(\mathbf{M}^{-1}u) = (\mathbf{LM}^{-1})u. \tag{13}$$

But from (11)

$$\mathbf{M}w = u \tag{14}$$

and from (12)

$$w = \mathbf{L}^{-1}v \tag{15}$$

since $w^{(k-1)}(x_0) = 0$, $1 \leqq k \leqq n$. Equations (14) and (15) imply

$$u = \mathbf{M}(\mathbf{L}^{-1}v) = (\mathbf{M}\mathbf{L}^{-1})v. \tag{16}$$

Equations (13) and (16) now yield the desired result:

$$\mathbf{L}\mathbf{M}^{-1} = (\mathbf{M}\mathbf{L}^{-1})^{-1}. \tag{17}$$

As a corollary, if we let $\mathbf{M} = \mathbf{I}$, we conclude from (17) that

$$\mathbf{L} = (\mathbf{L}^{-1})^{-1}. \tag{18}$$

The "converse" of the preceding problem is to establish the symbolic formula

$$(\mathbf{M}^{-1}\mathbf{L})^{-1} = \mathbf{L}^{-1}\mathbf{M}.$$

We shall do this. Let $\partial\mathbf{L} = n$, $\partial\mathbf{M} = m$, and let the coefficients of $\mathbf{L}$ and $\mathbf{M}$ be of class C^∞ on some closed finite interval I. Let the leading coefficients of $\mathbf{L}$ and $\mathbf{M}$ be non-vanishing on I.

Now let $u(x) \in C^m(I)$ and $u^{(k-1)}(x_0) = 0$, $1 \leqq k \leqq m$, for some point x_0 in I, and define $w(x)$ by the equation

$$w = \mathbf{M}u. \tag{19}$$

Also define $v(x)$ by the equation

$$v = \mathbf{L}^{-1}w. \tag{20}$$

Then $v(x) \in C^n(I)$ and $v^{(k-1)}(x_0) = 0$, $1 \leqq k \leqq n$. From (20) and (19)

$$v = \mathbf{L}^{-1}(\mathbf{M}u) = (\mathbf{L}^{-1}\mathbf{M})u. \tag{21}$$

But from (19)

$$u = \mathbf{M}^{-1}w \tag{22}$$

since $u^{(k-1)}(x_0) = 0$, $1 \leqq k \leqq m$, by hypothesis; and by (20)

$$w = \mathbf{L}v. \tag{23}$$

Hence (22) and (23) imply

$$u = \mathbf{M}^{-1}(\mathbf{L}v) = (\mathbf{M}^{-1}\mathbf{L})v. \tag{24}$$

From (21) and (24) we now infer

$$\mathbf{L}^{-1}\mathbf{M} = (\mathbf{M}^{-1}\mathbf{L})^{-1}. \tag{25}$$

Summarizing the above rcsults, including Theorem 2, we obtain the following theorem expressing sufficient conditions:

Theorem 3. Let $\mathbf{L}$ and $\mathbf{M}$ be linear differential operators of orders n and m respectively whose coefficients are of class C^∞ on some closed finite interval I. Let the leading coefficients of $\mathbf{L}$ and $\mathbf{M}$ be non-vanishing on I. Then for any function of class $C^\infty(I)$ which together with its first $n+m-1$ derivatives vanish at some point $x_0 \in I$:

(i) $\mathbf{L}^{-1}\mathbf{L} = \mathbf{L}\mathbf{L}^{-1} = \mathbf{I}$

(ii) $(\mathbf{L}\mathbf{M})^{-1} = \mathbf{M}^{-1}\mathbf{L}^{-1}$

(iii) $(\mathbf{L}\mathbf{M}^{-1})^{-1} = \mathbf{M}\mathbf{L}^{-1}$

(iv) $(\mathbf{L}^{-1}\mathbf{M})^{-1} = \mathbf{M}^{-1}\mathbf{L}$,

and all the above formulas are true if we interchange $\mathbf{L}$ and $\mathbf{M}$.

Equations (21) and (24) can be interpreted in terms of solving the differential equation

$$\mathbf{L}v = \mathbf{M}u. \tag{26}$$

If $u(x) \in C^m(I)$, then $\mathbf{M}u$ is a continuous function and

$$v = \mathbf{L}^{-1}\mathbf{M}u. \tag{27}$$

If $v(x) \in C^n(I)$ is given, then $\mathbf{L}v$ is a continuous function and

$$u = \mathbf{M}^{-1}\mathbf{L}v. \tag{28}$$

Thus we may "solve" (26) for either $v(x)$ or $u(x)$ by virtue of (27) or (28), depending on whether $u(x)$ or $v(x)$ is given. Sometimes we write (26) as

$$v = \frac{\mathbf{M}}{\mathbf{L}}u$$

(say when u is given). However, this is ambiguous since $\mathbf{M}/\mathbf{L}$ could be interpreted as $\mathbf{L}^{-1}\mathbf{M}$ or $\mathbf{M}\mathbf{L}^{-1}$, and in general $\mathbf{L}^{-1}\mathbf{M} \neq \mathbf{M}\mathbf{L}^{-1}$.

Suppose now $u^{(k-1)}(x_0)=0$ for $1 \leqq k \leqq m$ and $v^{(k-1)}(x_0)=0$ for $1 \leqq k \leqq n$. Then we may write either (27) or (28) with impunity. Let us interpret, say, (27) in terms of the Green's function. If $H(x,\xi)$ is the one-sided Green's function for **L**, then (27) may be written as

$$v(x) = \int_{x_0}^{x} H(x,\xi)\, \mathbf{M}u(\xi)\, d\xi. \tag{29}$$

Now if $n = \partial\mathbf{L}$ exceeds $m = \partial\mathbf{M}$, we may invoke Green's formula to write

$$\int_{x_0}^{x} [H(x,\xi)\, \mathbf{M}u(\xi) - u(\xi)\, \mathbf{M}_\xi^* H(x,\xi)]d\xi = \pi_\xi[u(\xi), H(x,\xi)]\Big|_{x_0}^{x}. \tag{30}$$

But $u^{(k)}(x_0) = 0$, $0 \leqq k \leqq m-1$, and $\left.\frac{\partial^k}{\partial \xi^k} H(x,\xi)\right|_{\xi = x} = 0$ for $0 \leqq k \leqq m - 1 \leqq n - 2$. Thus

$$\pi_\xi[u(x),\ H(x,x)] = 0 = \pi_\xi[u(x_0),\ H(x,x_0)]$$

and (30) becomes

$$\int_{x_0}^{x} H(x,\xi)\, \mathbf{M}u(\xi)\, d\xi = \int_{x_0}^{x} u(\xi)\, \mathbf{M}_\xi^* H(x,\xi)\, d\xi.$$

Equation (29) may therefore be written in the form

$$v(x) = \int_{x_0}^{x} \mathbf{M}_\xi^* H(x,\xi)\, u(\xi)\, d\xi. \tag{31}$$

Formalizing:

Theorem 4. Let **L** and **M** be linear differential operators of orders n and m respectively with $n > m$. Let the coefficients of **L** and **M** be of class C^∞ on some closed finite interval I. Let the leading coefficient of **L** be positive on I. Let $u(x)$ be any function of class $C^m(I)$ with the property that $u^{(k-1)}(x_0) = 0$, $1 \leqq k \leqq m$, for some $x_0 \in I$. Then the solution of the equation

$$\mathbf{L}v = \mathbf{M}u$$

may be written

$$v(x) = \int_{x_0}^{x} \mathbf{M}_\xi^* H(x,\xi)\, u(\xi)\, d\xi$$

where $H(x,\xi)$ is the one-sided Green's function for **L**, and **M*** is the adjoint of **M**.

3. Self-Adjoint Operators

We call a linear differential operator $\mathbf{L}$ of the nth order *formally self-adjoint* if $\mathbf{L}=(-1)^n\,\mathbf{L}^*$. Clearly $\mathbf{LL}^*$ is always formally self-adjoint since by Theorem 1 of Chapter 2,

$$(\mathbf{LL}^*)^* = \mathbf{L}^{**}\mathbf{L}^* = \mathbf{LL}^* = (-1)^{2n}\mathbf{LL}^*.$$

If $\mathbf{L}$ is self-adjoint and $H(x,\xi)$ is its Green's function, then by Theorem 4 of Chapter 3,

$$H(x,\xi) = (-1)^{n+1}\,H(\xi,x). \tag{1}$$

We shall deduce an important consequence of this identity.

Let

$$\mathbf{L} = p_0(x)\,\frac{d^n}{dx^n} + p_1(x)\,\frac{d^{n-1}}{dx^{n-1}} + \cdots + p_n(x)\cdot$$

where the $p_i(x)$, $0 \leqq i \leqq n$, are of class C^{n-i} on the closed finite interval I and $p_0(x) > 0$ on I. From (3.3.1) we may write the Green's function $H(x,\xi)$ of $\mathbf{L}$ as

$$H(x,\xi) = \tilde{\Phi}(x)\,\Phi^*(\xi)$$

where $\Phi(x)=\{\varphi_1(x),\ \varphi_2(x),\cdots,\ \varphi_n(x)\}$ is a column vector of the fundamental system $\{\varphi_j(x)|1 \leqq j \leqq n\}$ for $\mathbf{L}y=0$ and $\tilde{\Phi}(x)$, its transpose, is a row vector. Also $\Phi^*(\xi)=\{\varphi_1^*(\xi),\ \varphi_2^*(\xi),\cdots,\ \varphi_n^*(\xi)\}$ where the $\varphi_j^*(x)$, $1 \leqq j \leqq n$, form a fundamental set of solutions for $\mathbf{L}^*z=0$. Now if $\mathbf{L}$ is formally self-adjoint, the $\varphi_j^*(x)$ are linear combinations of the $\varphi_j(x)$ and conversely. Thus

$$\Phi^*(x) = C\,\Phi(x) \tag{2}$$

where C is a non-singular $n\times n$ matrix. Thus

$$H(x,\xi) = \tilde{\Phi}(x)C\Phi(\xi),$$

and, since H is a scalar,

$$H(x,\xi) = \tilde{\Phi}(\xi)\tilde{C}\Phi(x) \tag{3}$$

where $\tilde{C}$ is the transpose of C. By (1)

$$H(x,\xi) = (-1)^{n+1}\,\tilde{\Phi}(\xi)C\Phi(x). \tag{4}$$

Thus from (3) and (4) we infer

$$\tilde{C} = (-1)^{n+1} C.$$

In other words, *if* $\mathbf{L}$ *is formally self-adjoint,* C *is symmetric if* n *is odd and* C *is skew-symmetric if* n *is even.*

We shall now prove an interesting theorem concerning the factorization of a linear differential operator into self-adjoint operators of the second order.

Theorem 5. Let

$$\mathbf{L} = p_0(x) \frac{d^n}{dx^n} + p_1(x) \frac{d^{n-1}}{dx^{n-1}} + \cdots + p_n(x)\cdot$$

be a linear differential operator of even order $n=2r$. Let $p_i(x) \in C^{n-i}$, $0 \leqq i \leqq n$, on some closed finite interval I. Let $p_0(x) > 0$ on I. Then there exists a closed subinterval I' of I such that on I',

$$\mathbf{L} = f(x)\, \mathbf{P}_1 \mathbf{P}_2 \cdots \mathbf{P}_r$$

where the $\mathbf{P}_k$, $1 \leqq k \leqq r$, are second order formally self-adjoint linear differential operators and $f(x)$ is continuous on I'.

The theorem follows immediately by complete induction from Lemmas 1 and 2 below.

Lemma 1. Let

$$\mathbf{N} = \frac{d^n}{dx^n} + q_1(x) \frac{d^{n-1}}{dx^{n-1}} + \cdots + q_n(x)\cdot$$

be a linear differential operator where $q_i(x) \in C^0(I)$, $0 \leqq i \leqq n$. Then there exists a subinterval of I on which $\mathbf{N}$ has been the representation

$$\mathbf{N} = \mathbf{PM}$$

where $\mathbf{P}$ is formally self-adjoint and of the second order.

Proof. Let $\varphi_j(x)$, $1 \leqq j \leqq n$, be a fundamental system for $\mathbf{N}y=0$ with Wronskian $W(x)$. Then there exist $n-2$ functions, say $\varphi_j(x)$, $1 \leqq j \leqq n-2$, with Wronskian $\omega(x)$ not identically zero on I. Let $\omega(x) \neq 0$ on some closed subinterval of I. Define the linear differential operator $\mathbf{M}$ by the equation

$$\mathbf{M}u = \frac{1}{W(x)} \begin{vmatrix} \varphi_1(x) & \varphi_2(x) & \cdots & \varphi_{n-2}(x) & u \\ \varphi_1'(x) & \varphi_2'(x) & \cdots & \varphi_{n-2}'(x) & u' \\ . & . & . & . & . \\ \varphi_1^{(n-2)}(x) & \varphi_2^{(n-2)}(x) & \cdots & \varphi_{n-2}^{(n-2)}(x) & u^{(n-2)} \end{vmatrix} \tag{5}$$

$$\equiv s_2(x)\, u^{(n-2)} + s_3(x)\, u^{(n-3)} + \cdots + s_n(x)\, u.$$

Let

$$\mathbf{P} = a(x) \frac{d^2}{dx^2} + b(x) \frac{d}{dx} + c(x)\cdot$$

be so chosen that $\mathbf{PM} = \mathbf{N}$. Now

$$\mathbf{PM}u = as_2 u^{(n)} + [a(2s_2' + s_3) + bs_2]\, u^{(n-1)} + \cdots$$

$$\mathbf{N}u = u^{(n)} + q_1\, u^{(n-1)} + \cdots. \tag{6}$$

From (5)

$$s_2 = \frac{\omega}{W} \tag{7}$$

and

$$s_2\omega' + s_3\omega = 0. \tag{8}$$

Also from (6)

$$W' + q_1 W = 0. \tag{9}$$

If we compare coefficients in $\mathbf{PM}u$ and $\mathbf{N}u$ we obtain

$$as_2 = 1 \tag{10}$$

$$a(2s_2' + s_3) + bs_2 = q_1. \tag{11}$$

Eliminating ω from (7) and (8), we have

$$s_3 = -\frac{1}{W}(Ws_2)'$$

and from (9)

$$q_1 = -\frac{W'}{W}.$$

Substituting these last two identities in (11) yields

$$as_2' + bs_2 = \frac{W'}{W}(as_2 - 1).$$

An application of (10) implies

$$a'(x) = b(x)$$

and hence $\mathbf{P} = \mathbf{P}^*$.

Lemma 2. Let $\mathbf{L}$ be as in Theorem 5. Then there is a closed subinterval of I such that $\mathbf{L}$ has the representation

$$\mathbf{L} = \mathbf{SQ}$$

where $\mathbf{Q} = \mathbf{Q}^*$ is of the second order.

Proof. Let $\mathbf{N} = \dfrac{1}{p_0(x)}\mathbf{L}$. Then $\mathbf{N}$ is a linear differential operator with leading coefficient 1. Hence $\mathbf{N}^*$ has leading coefficient 1. By Lemma 1 there exists a subinterval of I such that $\mathbf{N}^* = \mathbf{QR}$ where $\mathbf{Q} = \mathbf{Q}^*$, and $\mathbf{Q}$ is of the second order. Taking adjoints of the above equation, we have

$$\mathbf{N} = \mathbf{R}^*\mathbf{Q}^* = \mathbf{R}^*\mathbf{Q}.$$

Now

$$\mathbf{L} = p_0(x)\mathbf{N} = p_0(x)\,\mathbf{R}^*\mathbf{Q}.$$

Let $p_0(x)\,\mathbf{R}^* = \mathbf{S}$. Then $\mathbf{L} = \mathbf{SQ}$.

4. Bilinear Forms

We recall (cf. Section 1 of Chapter 2) that the Lagrange concomitant was a bilinear form. It plays an important role in the theory of two-point boundary value problems to be discussed in Chapter 6. We shall therefore devote this section to the study of various algebraic properties of bilinear forms. First we give a general definition.

Definition. Let $A_n = \| a_{ij} \|_{1 \leqq i,\, j \leqq n}$ be a square matrix of rank $r \leqq n$. Let $X_n = \{x_1, x_2, \cdots, x_n\}$ and $Y_n = \{y_1, y_2, \cdots, y_n\}$ be n-dimensional column vectors. Let tildes denote transposes. Thus $\tilde{X}_n$, the transpose of X_n, is a row vector. Let

$$b(X_n, Y_n) = \tilde{X}_n A_n Y_n = \sum_{i=1}^{n} \sum_{j=1}^{n} x_i a_{ij} y_j.$$

Then $b(X_n, Y_n)$ is called a *bilinear form in* X_n and Y_n.

The rank of the bilinear form is the rank of the matrix A_n. If $r < n$, we call the form *singular*. If $r = n$, we call the form *ordinary* or *non-singular*.

From the theory of matrices we know that there exist non-singular $n \times n$ matrices P_n and Q_n such that

$$\tilde{P}_n A_n Q_n = J_n^{(r)}$$

where $J_n^{(r)}$ is the partitioned matrix

$$J_n^{(r)} = \left\| \begin{array}{c:c} E_r & 0_{r,n-r} \\ \hdashline 0_{n-r,r} & 0_{n-r,n-r} \end{array} \right\|$$

and $E_r = \|\delta_{ij}\|_{1 \leqq i,j \leqq r}$ is the $r \times r$ identity matrix, while $0_{s,t}$ is an $s \times t$ matrix with zeros everywhere. If we set

$$X_n = P_n U_n,$$

$$Y_n = Q_n V_n,$$

then

$$b(X_n, Y_n) = (\widetilde{P_n U_n}) A_n (Q_n V_n) = \tilde{U}_n (\tilde{P}_n A_n Q_n) V_n$$

$$= \tilde{U}_n J_n^{(r)} V_n = \tilde{U}_r V_r = \sum_{i=1}^{r} u_i v_i$$

where $U_p = \{u_1, u_2, \cdots, u_p\}$ and $V_p = \{v_1, v_2, \cdots, v_p\}$, $1 \leqq p \leqq n$.

Suppose now that b is ordinary. Then $\det A_n \neq 0$ and there exist non-singular square matrices P_n and Q_n such that

$$\tilde{P}_n A_n Q_n = E_n.$$

In fact, if P_n is arbitrary ($\det P_n \neq 0$), then Q_n is uniquely determined as $Q_n = (\tilde{P}_n A_n)^{-1}$. Thus

$$b(X_n, Y_n) = \tilde{X}_n A_n Y_n = \tilde{U}_n V_n = \sum_{i=1}^{n} u_i v_i.$$

Now let U_n be subjected to a linear transformation R_n which leaves the first p components of U_n invariant:

$$Z_n = R_n U_n, \qquad \det R_n \neq 0,$$

where

$$Z_p = U_p.$$

Let S_n be a non-singular linear transformation of V_n,

$$W_n = S_n V_n, \tag{1}$$

such that

$$\tilde{U}_n V_n = \tilde{Z}_n W_n.$$

Then

$$S_n \tilde{R}_n = E_n. \tag{2}$$

We shall show that the last $n-p$ components of W_n, that is, $W^*_{n-p} = \{w_{p+1}, w_{p+2}, \cdots, w_n\}$, are linear combinations *only* of the last $n-p$ components of V_n. In other words,

$$\begin{aligned} \tilde{Z}_n W_n &= \tilde{U}_n V_n \\ &= u_1 w_1 + u_2 w_2 + \cdots + u_p w_p + z_{p+1} v'_{p+1} + z_{p+2} v'_{p+2} + \cdots + z_n v'_n \end{aligned} \tag{3}$$

where $v'_{p+1}, v'_{p+2}, \cdots, v'_n$ are linear combinations of $v_{p+1}, v_{p+2}, \cdots, v_n$ only. Furthermore, $w_i = v_i + \Delta_i$, $1 \leqq i \leqq p$, where Δ_i is a linear combination of $v_{p+1}, v_{p+2}, \cdots, v_n$ only.

For R_n to preserve U_p we must have

$$R_n = \left\| \begin{array}{c|c} E_p & 0_{p,n-p} \\ \hline C_{n-p,p} & D_{n-p} \end{array} \right\|$$

where $C_{n-p,p}$ is an arbitrary $(n-p) \times p$ matrix and D_{n-p} is a non-singular $n-p$ square matrix. From (2) we must have

$$S_n = \left\| \begin{array}{c|c} E_p & -\tilde{C}_{n-p,p} \tilde{D}^{-1}_{n-p} \\ \hline 0_{n-p,p} & \tilde{D}^{-1}_{n-p} \end{array} \right\|. \tag{4}$$

Thus

$$W^*_{n-p} = \tilde{D}^{-1}_{n-p} V^*_{n-p}$$

where $V^*_{n-p} = \{v_{p+1}, v_{p+2}, \cdots, v_n\}$ is the last $n-p$ components of V_n and D_{n-p} is non-singular. Hence

$$\begin{aligned} \tilde{U}_n V_n &= \tilde{Z}_n W_n = \tilde{Z}_p W_p + \tilde{Z}^*_{n-p} W^*_{n-p} \\ &= \tilde{U}_p W_p + \tilde{Z}^*_{n-p} (\tilde{D}^{-1}_{n-p} V^*_{n-p}) \end{aligned}$$

which is (3).

We see, therefore, that changing the last $n-p$ components of U_n

does not affect the last $n-p$ components of V_n in the sense that the $v'_{p+1}, v'_{p+2}, \cdots, v'_n$ of (3) are linear combinations only of $v_{p+1}, v_{p+2}, \cdots, v_n$. Also, from (4)

$$W_p = V_p - \tilde{C}_{n-p,p}\tilde{D}_{n-p}^{-1}V_{n-p}^*$$

and w_i, $1 \leqq i \leqq p$, is equal to v_i plus a linear combination of $v_{p+1}, v_{p+2}, \cdots, v_n$.

Let us apply the above results to the Lagrange bilinear concomitant. From (2.1.5), $\pi[u,v]$ is a bilinear form in $u, u', \cdots, u^{(n-1)}$ and $v, v', \cdots, v^{(n-1)}$. Let

$$A_n = \|a_{ij}\|_{1 \leqq i,j \leqq n}$$

be the matrix of $\pi[u,v]$. Then

$$a_{i,n-i+1} = (-1)^{n-i}p_0(x), \qquad 1 \leqq i \leqq n,$$

are the terms on the secondary diagonal and the terms below the secondary diagonal are zero. Thus the determinant of this triangular matrix is

$$\det A_n = (-1)^{\frac{1}{2}n(n-1)}\, p_0^n(x).$$

Under our usual assumption that $p_0(x) \neq 0$ on some closed finite interval, we conclude that $\pi[u,v]$ is a non-singular bilinear form on this interval.

It will also be necessary in our future developments to consider the bilinear form

$$b(X_{2n}, Y_{2n}) = \pi[u(\xi),v(\xi)]\Big|_a^b = \pi[u(b),v(b)] - \pi[u(a), v(a)]$$

[cf. Green's formula, (2.1.4)]. We see that $b(X_{2n}, Y_{2n})$ is a bilinear form in

$$X_{2n} = \{u(a), u'(a), \cdots, u^{(n-1)}(a), u(b), u'(b), \cdots, u^{(n-1)}(b)\}$$

and

$$Y_{2n} = \{v(a), v'(a), \cdots, v^{(n-1)}(a), v(b), v'(b), \cdots, v^{(n-1)}(b)\}.$$

The determinant of the matrix of this bilinear form is $\pm p_0^{2n}(x) \neq 0$, and hence $b(X_{2n}, Y_{2n})$ is ordinary.

Let $U_1, U_2, \cdots, U_{2n}$ be any linearly independent combinations of the components of X_{2n}. That is,

$$\mathbf{U}_{2n} = P_{2n}X_{2n}$$

where P_{2n} is a $2n \times 2n$ non-singular square matrix and

$$\mathbf{U}_{2n} = \{U_1, U_2, \cdots, U_{2n}\}$$

is a $2n$-dimensional column vector. Then

$$b(X_{2n}, Y_{2n}) = U_1V_{2n} + U_2V_{2n-1} + \cdots + U_{2n}V_1 \tag{5}$$

where the V_i, $1 \leqq i \leqq 2n$, are uniquely determined linear combinations of the components of Y_{2n}.

5

DISTRIBUTION THEORY

1. Reasons for the Analysis

A. Let

$$\mathbf{L} = \frac{d^n}{dx^n} + p_1(x)\frac{d^{n-1}}{dx^{n-1}} + \cdots + p_n(x)\cdot \tag{1}$$

be a linear differential operator. If the coefficients $p_i(x)$, $1 \leqq i \leqq n$, are continuous on some closed finite interval $I=[a,b]$, then our basic theory guarantees the existence of a fundamental system of solutions. That is, there exist n linearly independent functions $\varphi_j(x)$, $1 \leqq j \leqq n$, with the property that $\mathbf{L}\varphi_j(x)=0$. Now in many practical problems the $p_i(x)$ coefficients are only piece-wise continuous. Thus the classical theory does not apply—at least not directly. Let us briefly analyze this situation.

Suppose for simplicity that the coefficients $p_i(x)$ of $\mathbf{L}$ are continuous except perhaps at a point c in (a,b) where one or more of the $p_i(x)$ may have a finite jump. On each of the closed intervals $[a,c]$ and $[c,b]$ we can solve the equation $\mathbf{L}y=0$. Thus there exist n functions $f_j(x)$, $1 \leqq j \leqq n$, which are linearly independent on $[a,c]$, have n continuous derivatives on $[a,c]$, and $\mathbf{L}f_j=0$, $1 \leqq j \leqq n$, on $[a,c]$. Similarly there exist n functions $g_j(x)$, $1 \leqq j \leqq n$, which are linearly independent on $[c,b]$, have n continuous derivatives on $[c,b]$, and $\mathbf{L}g_j=0$, $1 \leqq j \leqq n$, on $[c,b]$. Suppose

$$f_j^{(k-1)}(c) = a_{jk}, \qquad 1 \leqq j, k \leqq n.$$

Without loss of generality we may assume

$$g_j^{(k-1)}(c) = a_{jk}, \qquad 1 \leqq j, k \leqq n.$$

Now consider the n functions $h_j(x)$ defined as:

$$h_j(x) = \begin{cases} f_j(x), & a \leqq x \leqq c \\ & \qquad\qquad 1 \leqq j \leqq n \\ g_j(x), & c \leqq x \leqq b. \end{cases} \tag{2}$$

Then the $h_j(x)$ enjoy the following properties:

(i) The $h_j(x)$, $1 \leqq j \leqq n$, are linearly independent on $[a,b]$.

(ii) $\mathbf{L}h_j(x) = 0$ on $[a,c]$ and $[c,b]$, $1 \leqq j \leqq n$.

(iii) The $h_j(x)$, $1 \leqq j \leqq n$, have $n-1$ continuous derivatives on $[a,b]$.

This last statement is the crux of the matter. If the $h_j(x)$ do not have n continuous derivatives on I, then they cannot be solutions over $[a,b]$ of $\mathbf{L}y = 0$ in the classical sense. Yet they certainly are related intimately to $\mathbf{L}$.

In this section we wish to indicate various problems of the type illustrated above, that is, the failure of the classical theory when the functions involved in the discussion of linear differential operators are not sufficiently smooth. A satisfactory theory that enables us to treat such phenomena (and certain generalizations) will be developed in subsequent sections by the use of distribution theory.

B. Let us again consider (1) where we now assume the continuity of the coefficients $p_i(x)$ on I. Let $f(x) \in C^n([a,c])$ and $f(x) \in C^n([c,b])$. Then if $g(x)$ is defined by the equations

$$\mathbf{L}f = g, \qquad [a,c)$$

$$\mathbf{L}f = g, \qquad (c,b]$$

we see that

$$\mathbf{L}f = g, \qquad [a,b] \tag{3}$$

except perhaps at $x = c$. Arbitrarily defining $g(c)$, we are led to the truth of (3) where $g(x)$ is piece-wise continuous. Certainly such a problem is also intimately related to the classical theory.

C. Let us now make some interpretations regarding the one-sided Green's function. Suppose $\{\omega_j(x)|1 \leqq j \leqq n\}$ are n functions defined on $I=[a,b]$. Then we define

$$\Delta(\omega_1, \omega_2, \cdots, \omega_n|x,\xi) = \frac{(-1)^{n-1}}{W(\xi)} \begin{vmatrix} \omega_1(x) & \omega_2(x) & \cdots & \omega_n(x) \\ \omega_1(\xi) & \omega_2(\xi) & \cdots & \omega_n(\xi) \\ \omega_1'(\xi) & \omega_2'(\xi) & \cdots & \omega_n'(\xi) \\ \cdot & \cdot & \cdot & \cdot \\ \omega_1^{(n-2)}(\xi) & \omega_2^{(n-2)}(\xi) & \cdots & \omega_n^{(n-2)}(\xi) \end{vmatrix} \quad (4)$$

where $W(\xi)$ is the Wronskian of the $\omega_j(\xi)$, $1 \leqq j \leqq n$, whenever the right-hand side of (4) is meaningful. Now once more consider the operator $\mathbf{L}$ where the coefficients $p_i(x)$, $1 \leqq i \leqq n$, are continuous on I, except perhaps at a point $x=c$ in (a,b) where one or more of the $p_i(x)$ may have a finite jump. Then with the n functions $\{h_j(x)|1 \leqq j \leqq n\}$ of (2) we may construct $\Delta(h_1, h_2, \cdots, h_n|x,\xi)$ and this function is jointly continuous in x and ξ on $I \times I$. Clearly Δ is the one-sided Green's function for $\mathbf{L}$ on $[a,c]$ and $[c,b]$. Furthermore, since $\Delta(h_1, h_2, \cdots, h_n|x,\xi)$ is continuous on $I \times I$, the integral

$$\int_{x_0}^{x} \Delta(h_1, \cdots, h_n|x,\xi)\, g(\xi)\, d\xi, \qquad x_0, x \in I$$

defines a continuous function on I, say $f(x)$, for every continuous function $g(x)$ on I. Certainly $\mathbf{L}f=g$ on $[a,c]$ and $[c,b]$. What can be said about $\mathbf{L}f=g$ on $[a,b]$?

D. Finally, consider the case where the coefficients of $\mathbf{L}$ are continuous on I, but one or more of the $p_i(x)$ fail to be of class $C^{n-i}(I)$. Then we cannot construct the adjoint operator $\mathbf{L}^*$. Yet the one-sided Green's function $H(x,\xi)$ for $\mathbf{L}$ certainly exists and $K(x,\xi) = -H(\xi,x)$ is jointly continuous in x and ξ on $I \times I$. Hence for any function $g^*(x)$ which is integrable on I,

$$f^*(x) = \int_{x_0}^{x} K(x,\xi)\, g^*(\xi)\, d\xi, \qquad x_0, x \in I \qquad (5)$$

defines a continuous function $f^*(x)$ on I. What interpretation can be given to the equation $\mathbf{L}^*f^* = g^*$? [Clearly, if $p_i(x) \in C^{n-i}(I)$, $1 \leqq i \leqq n$, then $K(x,\xi) = H^*(x,\xi)$ by Theorem 4 of Chapter 3.] Another fact that lends credibility to the existence of such an interpretation is that in forming the adjoint in matrix form only the continuity of the $p_i(x)$ coefficients was used (cf. Section 3 of Chapter 2).

2. Linear Functionals

We inaugurate our discussion of distribution theory by a consideration of linear functionals. Let C be a linear vector space of functions and $\mathscr{R}$ the field of real numbers. Let μ be a mapping of C into $\mathscr{R}$:

$$\mu : C \longrightarrow \mathscr{R}.$$

Then we call μ a *functional* over C. Introduce a topology in C. If $\{\varphi_n(x)\}$ is a sequence of functions in C converging to zero in C-topology, then we say μ is *continuous* if $\{\mu\varphi_n\}$ converges to zero in the topology of the real numbers. If

$$\mu(a\varphi + b\psi) = a(\mu\varphi) + b(\mu\psi)$$

for all $a, b \in \mathscr{R}$ and $\varphi, \psi \in C$, then we call μ a *linear functional*. The The set of all linear functionals over C forms a space called the adjoint or dual of C.

For example, if C^0 is the space of functions continuous on [0,1] and $f(x)$ is a fixed continuous function, then

$$\mu\varphi = \int_0^1 f(x)\varphi(x)\,dx$$

for all $\varphi \in C^0$ defines a functional over C^0. Introduces a norm into C^0 by the definition

$$\| \varphi(x) \| = \max_{[0,1]} |\varphi(x)|.$$

Let $\{\varphi_n(x)\}$ be a sequence of functions which converges to zero in this topology, that is,

$$\lim_{n\to\infty} \| \varphi_n(x) \| = 0, \qquad \varphi_n \in C^0.$$

Now

$$\mu\varphi_n = \int_0^1 f(x)\, \varphi_n(x)\, dx$$

and if we let $M = \max_{[0,1]} |f(x)|$, then

$$|\mu\varphi_n| \leqq M\int_0^1 |\varphi_n(x)|\, dx \leqq M\|\varphi_n\|.$$

But $\{\mu\varphi_n\}$ is a sequence of real numbers converging to zero. Hence μ is a continuous functional. Also

$$\begin{aligned}\mu(a\varphi + b\psi) &= \int_0^1 f(x)[a\varphi(x) + b\psi(x)]\, dx \\ &= a\int_0^1 f(x)\varphi(x)\, dx + b\int_0^1 f(x)\psi(x)\, dx \\ &= a(\mu\varphi) + b(\mu\psi)\end{aligned}$$

for all $a, b \in \mathscr{R}$ and $\varphi, \psi \in C^0$. This implies that μ is a linear functional.

As a second example let

$$\nu\varphi = \varphi(\alpha)$$

in the space C^0 of continuous functions introduced above where α is a fixed real number, $0 \leqq \alpha \leqq 1$. Then ν is a functional over C^0. In the C^0-topology introduced above

$$|\nu\varphi_n| = |\varphi_n(\alpha)| \leqq \|\varphi_n(x)\|$$

and if $\{\varphi_n(x)\} \to 0$ in C^0-norm, then $\{\nu\varphi_n\} \to 0$ in the usual topology of the real numbers. Thus ν is a continuous functional. Clearly ν is linear since

$$\begin{aligned}\nu(a\varphi + b\psi) &= (a\varphi + b\psi)(\alpha) \\ &= a[\varphi(\alpha)] + b[\psi(\alpha)] \\ &= a(\nu\varphi) + b(\nu\psi).\end{aligned}$$

3. Fundamental Definitions

Let R be the real line, V an open set in R, and $C^0(V)$ the class of functions continuous on V. As we have done before, recursively define $C^k(V)$, $k \geqq 1$, as the class of all functions $f \in C^0(V)$ with the property that df/dx exists and belongs to $C^{k-1}(V)$. Clearly† $C^{k-1}(V) \supset C^k(V)$. We define $C^\infty(V)$ as

$$C^\infty(V) = \bigcap_{k \geqq 1} C^k(V).$$

Let $f \in C^0(V)$. The *support* or *carrier* of f (written Supp f) is the smallest closed set in R outside which $f=0$. That is, $x \in \operatorname{Supp} f$ if $f \not\equiv 0$ in any neighborhood of x. Conversely, if $f=0$ in some neighborhood of x then this implies and is implied by $x \notin \operatorname{Supp} f$. We define $C_C^k(V)$ as the set of all functions f belonging to $C^k(V)$ with compact support contained in V. Clearly $C_C^k(V) \subset C_C^k(R)$ if we define f as zero on the complement ${}^cV$ of V. We shall adopt this convention.

For simplicity in notation let $D_V = C_C^\infty(V)$. We now introduce a topology into D_V.

Definition. Let $\{\varphi_n(x)\}$ be a sequence of functions in D_V. We say $\{\varphi_n(x)\}$ *converges* to zero in D_V (written: $\{\varphi_n(x)\} \to 0$ in D_V) if:

(i) There exists a compact set K in V such that $\operatorname{Supp} \varphi_n \subset K$ for all n.

(ii) We have $\{\varphi_n^{(p)}(x)\} \to 0$ uniformly on K. That is,

$$\lim_{n\to\infty} \operatorname*{l.u.b.}_{x \in K} |\varphi_n^{(p)}(x)| = 0, \qquad \text{all } p.$$

We are now in a position to define *distribution.*

Definition. A *distribution* μ on the open set $V \subset R$ is a continuous linear functional defined for all φ in D_V.

(We recall that μ is continuous if $\{\varphi_n\} \to 0$ in D_V implies $\{\mu\varphi_n\} \to 0$ in the usual topology of the real numbers.)

We shall say $\{\varphi_n\} \to \varphi$ in D_V if $\{\varphi_n - \varphi\} \to 0$ in D_V. It follows immediately from the linearity of μ that if $\{\varphi_n\} \to \varphi$, then $\{\mu(\varphi_n - \varphi)\} \to 0$ implies $\{\mu\varphi_n\} \to \mu\varphi$. If μ is a distribution with the property that $\mu\varphi = 0$ for all $\varphi \in D_V$, then we shall call μ the *zero distribution* and write $\mu = 0$. It will suffice for our purposes to assume that V is an open *interval* in R.

---

† If A and B are any two sets with the property that every element of A is in B we write $A \subset B$ or $B \supset A$.

4. Functions with Compact Support

We wish to show that the class of functions D_V is not vacuous. Let

$$f(x) = e^{-1/x}, \qquad x > 0$$
$$f(x) = 0, \qquad x \leqq 0.$$

Then

$$\frac{d^k f}{dx^k} = P_k\left(\frac{1}{x}\right) e^{-1/x}, \qquad x > 0$$

$$\frac{d^k f}{dx^k} = 0, \qquad x < 0$$

where $P_k(\xi)$ is a polynomial in ξ. Define

$$\left.\begin{aligned} f_k &= \frac{d^k f}{dx^k}, \qquad x \neq 0 \\ f_k &= 0, \qquad x = 0. \end{aligned}\right\} \quad k \geqq 0$$

Since

$$\lim_{\substack{x \to 0 \\ x > 0}} P_k\left(\frac{1}{x}\right) e^{-1/x} = 0$$

for all k we infer that f_k is continuous on R. Thus

$$\frac{d}{dx} f_{k-1} = f_k$$

for all x and $f_k \in C^\infty(R)$. In particular, $f_0 \equiv f \in C^\infty(R)$.

Consider, for example,

$$\varphi(x) = f(x-a)\, f(b-x)$$

where $b > a$. Then $\varphi \in C^\infty(R)$ and Supp $\varphi = [a,b]$. Thus $\varphi \in C_C^\infty(R)$.

Other simple examples may be constructed. For example,

$$\begin{aligned} \psi(x) &= \exp\left[-(x-a)^{-2} - (x-b)^{-2}\right] \qquad & a < x < b \\ &= 0, & \text{otherwise} \end{aligned}$$

is in $C^\infty(R)$ and Supp $\psi = [a,b]$.

5. Examples of Distributions

We shall now consider some examples of distributions. Let f be piece-wise continuous on every compact subinterval K of the open interval V. Then we shall say that $f(x)$ is *locally summable* on V. It follows that $\int_K |f| \, dx < \infty$. Now define a mapping μ_f of D_V into R by the equation

$$\mu_f \varphi = \int f(x)\varphi(x) \, dx, \qquad \varphi \in D_V. \tag{1}$$

(All integrals will be assumed to be from $-\infty$ to $+\infty$ unless otherwise indicated.) We assert that μ_f is a distribution.

First we see that μ_f is well defined. For, let $K = \text{Supp } \varphi$. Since φ is continuous on a compact set, $M = \max_K |\varphi|$ is finite. Thus

$$\int_K |f(x)\varphi(x)| \, dx \leqq M \int_K |f(x)| \, dx < \infty.$$

Secondly, μ_f is linear. This follows immediately from the linearity of the integral. Thirdly, μ_f is continuous.

To prove this, let J be any compact set containing Supp φ. Then

$$|\mu_f \varphi| \leqq \int_J |f\varphi| \, dx \leqq M \int_J |f(x)| \, dx.$$

Now let $\{\varphi_n\}$ be a sequence of functions in D_V converging to zero. Then there exists a compact set, say J, such that Supp $\varphi_n \subset J$ for all n. Thus

$$|\mu_f \varphi_n| \leqq \underset{x \in J}{\text{l.u.b.}} \, |\varphi_n| \int_J |f(x)| \, dx.$$

But $\lim_{n \to \infty} \text{l.u.b.}_{x \in J} |\varphi_n| = 0$ if $\{\varphi_n\} \to 0$ in D_V. Since $\int_J |f(x)| \, dx$ is a finite constant, $\{\mu_f \varphi_n\} \to 0$ in the usual topology of the real number system. We have proved, therefore:

Theorem 1. Every locally summable function f on V defines a distribution μ_f over D_V.

The distribution μ_f of the above theorem is unique. For suppose there existed a locally summable function g such that $\mu_f \varphi = \mu_g \varphi$ for all

$\varphi \in D_V$. Then this would imply $\mu_{f-g}\varphi = 0$ or $\mu_{f-g} = 0$. Thus it suffices to prove:

Theorem 2. If $\mu_f = 0$, then $f = 0$ almost everywhere.

Proof. If $f = 0$ at every point of continuity of f, then clearly $f = 0$ a.e. Suppose x_0 is a point of continuity of f at which $f(x_0) \neq 0$. Since f is piece-wise continuous there exists a neighborhood $J = [a,b]$ of x_0 in V such that $f(x) \neq 0$ in J. Let $\varphi \neq 0$ be in D_V with support J. Then

$$\mu_f\varphi = \int f\varphi \, dx = \int_J f\varphi \, dx \neq 0$$

which contradicts the assumption that $\mu_f\varphi = 0$ for all $\varphi \in D_V$.

As another example of a distribution let us define a mapping ϵ of D_V into R by the equation

$$\epsilon\varphi = \varphi^{(p)}(\alpha), \qquad \varphi \in D_V$$

where α is a fixed point in R and p is a fixed integer. We assert that ϵ is a distribution. First

$$\begin{aligned} \epsilon(a\varphi + b\psi) &= (a\varphi + b\psi)^{(p)}(\alpha) \\ &= a[\varphi^{(p)}(\alpha)] + b[\psi^{(p)}(\alpha)] \\ &= a(\epsilon\varphi) + b(\epsilon\psi) \end{aligned}$$

for all $a, b \in R$ and $\varphi, \psi \in D_V$. Hence ϵ is a linear functional. Also, if $\{\varphi_n(x)\} \to 0$ in D_V then $\{\varphi_n^{(p)}(\alpha)\}$ clearly converges to zero in the topology of the real numbers. But

$$\epsilon\varphi_n = \varphi_n^{(p)}(\alpha).$$

Hence $\{\epsilon\varphi_n\} \to 0$ and ϵ is a continuous functional. These two results imply that ϵ is a distribution on V.

If μ is any distribution, then we say μ is a *function* if there exists a locally summable function f such that $\mu = \mu_f$ in the sense of (1). Thus every function is a distribution. The converse is not true. For example, ϵ is not a function.

6. The Dirac Functional

Let us rewrite (5.1) as

$$f\varphi = \int f(x)\varphi(x) \, dx, \qquad \varphi \in D_V \tag{1}$$

where $f(x)$ is locally summable on V. We have seen that f is a distribution. We do not distinguish between the *distribution* f [on the left-hand side of (1)] and the *function* $f(x)$ [on the right-hand side of (1)]. A function has values; a distribution does not have values unless it is a function.

If $f(x)$ has a continuous derivative, then the usual formula for integration by parts yields

$$\int f(x)\varphi'(x)\,dx = -\int f'(x)\varphi(x)\,dx. \tag{2}$$

In the functional notation

$$f\varphi' = \int f(x)\varphi'(x)\,dx = -\int f'(x)\varphi(x)\,dx = -f'\varphi. \tag{3}$$

(Clearly $\varphi' \in D_V$.) We call the distribution f' the *derivative* of the distribution f. That is, f' is defined by the equation

$$f'\varphi = -\int f(x)\varphi'(x)\,dx. \tag{4}$$

In this example f' also exists as a function.

Suppose now that $f(x)$ is locally summable on V. Then $f'(x)$ does not necessarily exist as a function and the formula (2) for integration by parts is not necessarily valid. However, $\int f(x)\varphi'(x)\,dx$ *is* a meaningful expression. Thus if we define a functional g by the equation

$$g\varphi = -\int f(x)\varphi'(x)\,dx, \qquad \varphi \in D_V \tag{5}$$

then g is a continuous linear functional; that is, g is a distribution on V. We shall call g the *derivative* of the distribution f and write $g = f'$. In other words, the right-hand side of (4) defines a distribution f' called the derivative of f regardless of whether the function $f(x)$ has a derivative or not. If $f'(x)$ is locally summable, then the definition of the derivative of $f(x)$ coincides with the definition of the derivative of the distribution.

Because the functional notation is so convenient we shall often write (3) even if $f'(x)$ is *not* a function. In these cases we shall call $f'(x)$ a *symbolic function* and say it is the *symbolic derivative* of $f(x)$. We cannot speak of the *values* attained by $f'(x)$; its only meaning is through the defining equation

$$\int f'(x)\varphi(x)\,dx = -\int f(x)\varphi'(x)\,dx$$

and the right-hand side of this equation *is* defined.

We have defined the symbolic derivative of a locally summable function by (2). Considering f as a distribution, its derivative is the distribution f' given by (4). Inductively we define the pth derivative of a distribution f by

$$f^{(p)}\varphi = \int f^{(p)}(x)\varphi(x)\,dx = -\int f^{(p-1)}(x)\varphi'(x)\,dx = -f^{(p-1)}\varphi' \qquad (6)$$

for $p \geqq 1$ and call $f^{(p)}(x)$ the *pth* symbolic derivative of $f(x)$.

Consider now the unit step function $u(x-a)$ where a is a fixed point in R:

$$u(x-a) = 0, \qquad x < a$$
$$u(x-a) = 1, \qquad x > a.$$

Then $u(x-a)$ is locally summable on R and hence defines a distribution u_a by the equation

$$u_a\varphi = \int u(x-a)\varphi(x)\,dx = \int_a^\infty \varphi(x)\,dx, \qquad \varphi \in D_V.$$

The symbolic derivative u_a' of u_a is defined by the equation

$$u_a'\varphi = -\int u(x-a)\varphi'(x)\,dx = \varphi(a). \qquad (7)$$

Merely as a change in notation write $\delta_a \equiv u_a'$. Then

$$\delta_a\varphi = \varphi(a). \qquad (8)$$

Note that δ_a is a distribution and *not* a function. We call $\delta(x-a)$ the symbolic derivative of $u(x-a)$ and write [cf. (3) and (8)]

$$\begin{aligned} u_a'\varphi &= -\int u(x-a)\varphi'(x)\,dx = \int \delta(x-a)\varphi(x)\,dx \\ &= \delta_a\varphi = \varphi(a). \end{aligned} \qquad (9)$$

Although as we have said earlier $\delta(x-a)$ is not a function, common usage calls $\delta(x-a)$ the *Dirac delta function* or *unit impulse function.* The delta function does not have values. It only has meaning when multiplied by a function $\varphi(x)$ in D_V, integrated from $-\infty$ to $+\infty$ and evaluated by (9); viz.:

$$\int \delta(x-a)\varphi(x)\,dx = \delta_a\varphi = \varphi(a).$$

The derivative of the δ-functional is defined by

$$\begin{aligned} \delta_a'\varphi &= \int \delta'(x-a)\varphi(x)\,dx = -\int \delta(x-a)\varphi'(x)\,dx \\ &= -\delta_a\varphi' = -\varphi'(a). \end{aligned} \qquad (10)$$

In general, from (6),

$$\delta_a^{(p)}\varphi = (-1)^p\, \delta_a\varphi^{(p)} = (-1)^p\, \varphi^{(p)}(a)$$

and in terms of the distribution ϵ introduced at the end of the preceding section,

$$\delta_\alpha^{(p)} = (-1)^p\, \epsilon.$$

7. Equations Involving Distributions

Let $V=(a,b)$ be an open interval in R. Let x_i, $1 \leqq i \leqq n$, be n distinct points in V such that

$$a < x_1 < x_2 < \cdots < x_n < b.$$

Let $f(x)$ be a function defined and continuous on (x_i, x_{i+1}), $0 \leqq i \leqq n$. (For symmetry in notation we have set $a=x_0$ and $b=x_{n+1}$.) Let

$$\lim_{\substack{x\to x_i\\ x<x_i}} f(x) \qquad \text{and} \qquad \lim_{\substack{x\to x_i\\ x>x_i}} f(x)$$

both exist for $1 \leqq i \leqq n$ and call the limits $f(x_i-)$ and $f(x_i+)$ respectively. Then we shall say $f(x)$ is *piece-wise* continuous on V.

More generally, suppose there exists a finite set of points x_i, $1 \leqq i \leqq n$, in V with

$$a < x_1 < x_2 < \cdots < x_n < b$$

such that

(i) $f(x) \in C^k((x_i,x_{i+1}))$, $\qquad 0 \leqq i \leqq n$

(ii) $\lim\limits_{\substack{x\to x_i\\ x<x_i}} f^{(k)}(x)$ and $\lim\limits_{\substack{x\to x_i\\ x>x_i}} f^{(k)}(x)$ both exist for $1 \leqq i \leqq n$.

We write these limits as $f^{(k)}(x_i-)$ and $f^{(k)}(x_i+)$ respectively. Then we say $f(x)$ is *piece-wise* k-*fold differentiable* on V.

Let $F_1(x)$ be a linear combination of the δ-distribution and its derivatives with sufficiently smooth functions as coefficients. Let $F_2(x)$ be a linear combination of symbolic derivatives of locally summable functions, also with sufficiently smooth functions as coefficients. For example,

$$F_1(x) = \sum_{i=1}^{n} \psi_i(x)\, \delta^{(p_i)}(x-a_i)$$

$$F_2(x) = \sum_{i=1}^{m} \chi_i(x)\, f_i^{(q_i)}(x)$$

where the f_i are locally summable and $\psi_i, \chi_i \in C^k(V)$ for some sufficiently large k. Let $F(x) = F_1(x) + F_2(x)$. Then we shall say $F(x)=0$ is a true equation in the sense of distributions, written

$$[\![\, F(x) = 0 \,]\!]$$

if

$$\int F(x)\varphi(x)\, dx = 0 \tag{1}$$

is a true equation involving ordinary functions for all $\varphi \in D_V$. In the evaluation of this integral we use

$$\int \delta^{(p)}(x-a)\varphi(x)\, dx = (-1)^p \varphi^{(p)}(a), \qquad p \geqq 0 \tag{2}$$

to define the distribution $\delta_a^{(p)}$ and use the formula

$$\int f^{(q)}(x)\varphi(x)\, dx = (-1)^q \int f(x)\varphi^{(q)}(x)\, dx \tag{3}$$

to define the symbolic derivatives $f^{(q)}$. (By $f', f'', \cdots, f^{(q)}, \cdots$ we always mean symbolic derivatives in the sense of distributions since otherwise the symbols would not necessarily be defined. In the case where the symbolic derivatives are ordinary functions, then the symbolic derivative is the ordinary derivative.)

It may be that $\int F(x)\varphi(x)\, dx=0$ for all $\varphi \in C_C^k(V)$ for some finite k. That is, $[\![\, F(x)=0 \,]\!]$ for a larger class of functions than $C_C^\infty(V)=D_V$. For example, ϵ is a functional defined on $C_C^p(V)$. If this be the case we shall tacitly use the larger space in (1), (2), and (3) above.

As a consequence of the linearity of the integral we may conclude that

$$[\![\, F(x) + G(x) = 0 \,]\!] \tag{4}$$

from the two statements $[\![\, F(x)=0 \,]\!]$ and $[\![\, G(x)=0 \,]\!]$ where $F(x)$ and $G(x)$ are linear combinations of $\delta^{(p)}$ and symbolic derivatives.

As an example, we assert

$$[\![\, x\delta(x) = 0 \,]\!];$$

that is, $x\delta(x)=0$ is a true equation in the sense of distributions. To prove this we need merely write, using (2),

$$\int x\delta(x)\varphi(x)\,dx = \int \delta(x)[x\varphi(x)]\,dx = [x\varphi(x)]\,|_{x=0} = 0.$$

As another example, we assert

$$[\![\ \nu(x) = \frac{d}{dx}|x|\ ]\!]$$

where $\nu(x) = +1$ for $x > 0$ and $\nu(x) = -1$ for $x < 0$. By (3)

$$\begin{aligned}\int |x|'\varphi(x)\,dx &= -\int |x|\varphi'(x)\,dx \\ &= -\int_{-\infty}^{0}(-x)\varphi'(x)\,dx - \int_{0}^{\infty} x\varphi'(x)\,dx \\ &= +\int_{-\infty}^{0} x\varphi'(x)\,dx - \int_{0}^{\infty} x\varphi'(x)\,dx \\ &= -\int_{-\infty}^{0} \varphi(x)\,dx + \int_{0}^{\infty} \varphi(x)\,dx \\ &= \int \nu(x)\varphi(x)\,dx.\end{aligned}$$

This last example can be generalized. Let $f(x)$ be continuous on V and have a piece-wise continuous derivative. Then $f'(x)$ may not exist on V in the classical sense. Let $\hat{f}'(x)$ equal the derivative of $f(x)$ at all points where $f(x)$ *does* have a derivative in the classical sense. Then $\hat{f}'(x)$ is an ordinary function. As usual let $f'(x)$ denote the symbolic derivative of $f(x)$. Then we assert that

$$[\![\ \hat{f}'(x) = f'(x)\ ]\!]. \tag{5}$$

For concreteness let $x=a$ be the only point at which $f'(x)$ does not exist. Then

$$\begin{aligned}\int f'(x)\varphi(x)\,dx &= -\int f(x)\varphi'(x)\,dx \\ &= -\int_{-\infty}^{a} f(x)\varphi'(x)\,dx - \int_{a}^{\infty} f(x)\varphi'(x)\,dx\end{aligned}$$

$$= -f(a)\varphi(a) + \int_{-\infty}^{a} \hat{f}'(x)\varphi(x)\,dx$$

$$+f(a)\varphi(a) + \int_{a}^{\infty} \hat{f}'(x)\varphi(x)\,dx$$

$$= \int \hat{f}'(x)\varphi(x)\,dx.$$

This result can be generalized even further. Let $f(x)$ be piece-wise differentiable on (a,b), differentiable on (a,c) and (c,b) and let $j = f(c+) - f(c-)$. Then $f'(x)$ exists on $V = (a,b)$ except at $x = c$, and we assert

$$[\![\, f'(x) = \hat{f}'(x) + j\delta(x-c) \,]\!]. \tag{6}$$

For from (3)

$$\int f'(x)\varphi(x)\,dx = -\int f(x)\varphi'(x)\,dx$$

$$= -\int_{-\infty}^{c} f(x)\varphi'(x)\,dx - \int_{c}^{\infty} f(x)\varphi'(x)\,dx$$

$$= -f(c-)\varphi(c) + \int_{-\infty}^{c} \hat{f}'(x)\varphi(x)\,dx$$

$$+f(c+)\varphi(c) + \int_{c}^{\infty} \hat{f}'(x)\varphi(x)\,dx$$

$$= j\varphi(c) + \int_{-\infty}^{\infty} \hat{f}'(x)\varphi(x)\,dx. \tag{7}$$

But from (2)

$$\varphi(c) = \int \delta(x-c)\varphi(x)\,dx.$$

Thus (7) becomes

$$\int f'(x)\varphi(x)\,dx = j\int \delta(x-c)\varphi(x)\,dx + \int \hat{f}'(x)\varphi(x)\,dx$$

$$= \int [j\,\delta(x-c) + \hat{f}'(x)]\,\varphi(x)\,dx$$

which is (6). [We have omitted such details as

$$\int_{-\infty}^{c} f(x)\varphi'(x)\,dx = \lim_{\substack{\epsilon\to 0\\ \epsilon>0}} \int_{-\infty}^{c-\epsilon} f(x)\varphi'(x)\,dx$$

$$= \lim_{\substack{\epsilon\to 0\\ \epsilon>0}} \left\{ [f(x)\varphi(x)]\Big|_{-\infty}^{c-\epsilon} - \int_{-\infty}^{c-\epsilon} f'(x)\varphi(x)\,dx \right\}$$

$$= \lim_{\substack{\epsilon\to 0\\ \epsilon>0}} \{f(c-\epsilon)\varphi(c-\epsilon)\} - \int_{-\infty}^{c} \hat{f}'(x)\varphi(x)\,dx.$$

But by definition of a piece-wise continuous function $\lim_{\epsilon\to 0,\epsilon>0} f(c-\epsilon)$ exists and equals $f(c-)$.]

If we have an equation $H(x) = 0$ involving the ordinary functions $\hat{f}^{(p)}(x)$, $\hat{g}^{(q)}(x)$, etc., then we understand this equation to be true only for those values of x for which *all* of the terms $\hat{f}^{(p)}(x)$, $\hat{g}^{(q)}(x)$, etc., are defined. From $H(x)=0$, of course, follows,

$$[\![\ H(x) = 0\ ]\!].$$

8. Distribution Theory of Differential Equations

Let

$$\mathbf{L} = \frac{d^n}{dx^n} + p_1(x)\frac{d^{n-1}}{dx^{n-1}} + \cdots + p_n(x). \tag{1}$$

be a linear differential operator where the $p_i(x)$, $1 \leqq i \leqq n$, are piece-wise continuous on the closed finite interval I. If $f(x) \in C^n(I)$; then operating with $\mathbf{L}$ on $f(x)$ yields a piece-wise continuous function $g(x)$,

$$\mathbf{L}f = g.$$

If $f(x)$ is piece-wise n-fold differentiable on I, then

$$\hat{\mathbf{L}}f = g \tag{2}$$

is a true equation where

$$\hat{\mathbf{L}}f \equiv \hat{f}^{(n)} + p_1(x)\hat{f}^{(n-1)} + \cdots + p_n(x)\hat{f}.$$

We wish to show that (2) implies

$$[\![\ \mathbf{L}f = g\ ]\!]. \tag{3}$$

Let $f(x) \in C^{n-1}(I)$ and be piece-wise n-fold differentiable on I. Then (2) holds, and since $f \in C^{n-1}(I)$,

$$\hat{f}^{(k)}(x) = f^{(k)}(x), \qquad 0 \leqq k \leqq n-1. \tag{4}$$

From (7.5)

$$[\![\hat{f}^{(n)}(x) = f^{(n)}(x)]\!]. \tag{5}$$

Certainly (2) implies

$$[\![\hat{\mathbf{L}}f = g]\!]$$

and (5) implies

$$[\![f^{(n)} - \hat{f}^{(n)} = 0]\!].$$

From these last two equations we conclude by (7.4) that

$$[\![f^{(n)} + p_1(x)\hat{f}^{(n-1)} + \cdots + p_n(x)\hat{f} = g(x)]\!]$$

and by (4)

$$[\![f^{(n)} + p_1(x) f^{(n-1)} + \cdots + p_n(x) f = g(x)]\!]$$

which is (3). This answers question **1B**.

Let $\mathbf{L}$ be as in (1) where the $p_i(x)$ are piece-wise continuous on the closed finite interval $I=[a,b]$. Let $\xi_1, \xi_2, \cdots, \xi_m$ where

$$a < \xi_1 < \xi_2 < \cdots < \xi_m < b$$

be the points at which at least one $p_i(x)$ is not continuous. Then all the $p_i(x)$ are continuous on the closed intervals $[\xi_i, \xi_{i+1}]$, $0 \leqq i \leqq m$. For uniformity in notation we have set $\xi_0 = a$ and $\xi_{m+1} = b$. Thus there exist n linearly independent functions

$$f_{1i}, f_{2i}, \cdots, f_{ni}, \qquad 0 \leqq i \leqq m,$$

defined on $[\xi_i, \xi_{i+1}]$ such that $\mathbf{L} f_{ji} = 0$, $1 \leqq j \leqq n$, for all $x \in [\xi_i, \xi_{i+1}]$ (and whose Wronskian does not vanish on $[\xi_i, \xi_{i+1}]$). Furthermore, $f_{ji}(x) \in C^n([\xi_i, \xi_{i+1}])$, $1 \leqq j \leqq n$. Let $f_{j0}^{(k-1)}(x)$, $1 \leqq j, k \leqq n$ assume the values a_{jk} at $x = \xi_1$. Let $f_{j1}^{(k-1)}(x)$ be defined so that $f_{j1}^{(k-1)}(\xi_1) = a_{jk}$, etc. In this way we obtain n functions $\{f_j(x) | 1 \leqq j \leqq n\}$ such that

(i) The Wronskian of the $\{f_j(x) | 1 \leqq j \leqq n\}$ does not vanish on I.

(ii) $f_j(x) = f_{ji}(x)$ for $x \in [\xi_i, \xi_{i+1}]$, $1 \leqq j \leqq n$, $\quad 0 \leqq i \leqq m$.

(iii) $f_j(x) \in C^{n-1}(I)$, $1 \leqq j \leqq n$.

(iv) The $\{f_j(x) | 1 \leqq j \leqq n\}$ are piece-wise n-fold differentiable on I.

(v) $\hat{\mathbf{L}} f_j(x) = 0, \ x \in I, \ 1 \leqq j \leqq n.$

Also we can define $f_j(x)$, $1 \leqq j \leqq n$, on $V-I$, where $V \supset I$ is an open set such that the $f_j(x)$ are of class C^n on the closure of $V-I$. It follows from (3) that

$$[\![\mathbf{L} f_j(x) = 0]\!], \qquad 1 \leqq j \leqq n. \tag{6}$$

Thus question **1A** is settled.

We now turn to a consideration of the inverse operator. Let $\mathbf{L}$ be as in (1). With the $f_j(x)$, $1 \leqq j \leqq n$, functions constructed in the preceding paragraph we may form

$$K(x,\xi) = \Delta(f_1, f_2, \cdots, f_n | x, \xi),$$

[cf. (1.4)]. Let $g(x)$ be continuous on I and consider

$$f(x) = \int_{x_0}^{x} K(x,\xi) g(\xi)\, d\xi, \qquad x_0, x \in I.$$

Now

$$f^{(k)}(x) = \int_{x_0}^{x} K_k(x,\xi)\, g(\xi)\, d\xi, \qquad 0 \leqq k \leqq n-1, \tag{7}$$

where we are again using the convention $K_k(x,\xi) = \partial^k K(x,\xi)/\partial x^k$. Also

$$\left[\!\!\left[\frac{d}{dx} \int_{x_0}^{x} K_{n-1}(x,\xi)\, g(\xi)\, d\xi = g(x) + \int_{x_0}^{x} \hat{K}_n(x,\xi)\, g(\xi)\, d\xi \right]\!\!\right] \tag{8}$$

by (7.5) and

$$\left[\!\!\left[\int_{x_0}^{x} \hat{K}_n(x,\xi)\, g(\xi)\, d\xi = \int_{x_0}^{x} K_n(x,\xi)\, g(\xi)\, d\xi \right]\!\!\right]. \tag{9}$$

Equations (7), (8) and (9) imply $\left[\!\!\left[\mathbf{L} f(x) = g(x) + \int_{x_0}^{x} \hat{\mathbf{L}}_x K(x,\xi)\, g(\xi) d\xi \right]\!\!\right]$

or

$$[\![\mathbf{L} f(x) = g(x)]\!] \tag{10}$$

which answers **1C**.

To answer question **1D** we must consider the adjoint operator $\mathbf{L}^*$. Let $\mathbf{L}$ be as in (1). The $\{f_j(x)|1 \leqq j \leqq n\}$ defined earlier have the property that $f_j(x) \in C^{n-1}(I)$ and are piece-wise of class $C^n(I)$ where I is the closed interval $[a,b]$. Let

$$K(x,\xi) = \Delta(f_1, f_2, \cdots, f_n|x,\xi).$$

and let $g^*(x)$ be continuous on I. We now define $f^*(x)$ as

$$f^*(x) = -\int_a^x K(\xi,x)\, g^*(\xi)\, d\xi \tag{11}$$

and assert that

$$[\![\mathbf{L}^*f^* = g^*]\!]. \tag{12}$$

Note that the right-hand side of (11) defines a continuous function, f^*.

A typical term of $\mathbf{L}^*f^*$ is $(-1)^k(p_{n-k}f^*)^{(k)}$. Since p_{n-k} is only piece-wise continuous this derivative must, in general, be interpreted as a symbolic derivative. As such it is defined by

$$(-1)^k \int (p_{n-k}f^*)^{(k)}\varphi\, dx = \int p_{n-k}(x) f^*(x)\, \varphi^{(k)}(x)\, dx \tag{13}$$

where $\varphi \in D_V$ and $V = (a, b)$. Summing (13) over k we obtain

$$\int (\mathbf{L}^*f^*)\varphi\, dx = \int f^*(\mathbf{L}\varphi)\, dx.$$

Now from (11)

$$\int (\mathbf{L}^*f^*)\varphi\, dx = -\int \left[\int_a^x K(\xi,x)\, g^*(\xi)\, d\xi\right] \mathbf{L}\varphi(x)\, dx$$

$$= -\int g^*(\xi)\, d\xi \int_\xi^b K(\xi,x)\, \mathbf{L}\varphi(x)\, dx$$

on interchanging the order of integration. Thus

$$\int (\mathbf{L}^*f^*)\varphi\, dx = \int g^*(\xi)\, d\xi \int_b^\xi K(\xi,x)\, \mathbf{L}\varphi(x)\, dx. \tag{14}$$

Let

$$\psi(\xi) = \int_b^\xi K(\xi,x)\, \mathbf{L}\varphi(x)\, dx. \tag{15}$$

Then from (10), we infer

$$[\![\mathbf{L}\psi = \mathbf{L}\varphi]\!]. \tag{16}$$

We assert that the above equation implies $\psi(x) = \varphi(x)$. For suppose $\psi \neq \varphi$. Since $[\![\mathbf{L}\psi = \mathbf{L}\varphi]\!]$ we must have

$$\psi = \varphi + \sum_{j=1}^{n} a_j f_j$$

where the a_j are constants. Now $\psi^{(k-1)}(b) = 0$, $1 \leqq k \leqq n$, by (15) and $\varphi^{(k-1)}(b) = 0$, $1 \leqq k \leqq n$, since φ has compact support interior to I. Thus

$$\sum_{j=1}^{n} a_j f_j^{(k-1)}(b) = 0, \qquad 1 \leqq k \leqq n.$$

But the Wronskian of the $\{f_j(x)\}$ is unequal to zero on I. Hence $a_j = 0$, $1 \leqq j \leqq n$. (This also shows that the double brackets in (16) may be dropped since ψ must also be in D_V.)

Since $\varphi(x) = \psi(x)$, equation (14) implies

$$\int (\mathbf{L}^* f^*)\varphi \, dx = \int g^*(\xi)\varphi(\xi) \, d\xi$$

which is (12).

9. Elementary Solutions

Let

$$\mathbf{L} = \frac{d^n}{dx^n} + p_1(x) \frac{d^{n-1}}{dx^{n-1}} + \cdots + p_n(x). \tag{1}$$

where for simplicity we shall assume the $p_i(x)$, $1 \leqq i \leqq n$, are continuous on I. We shall call $h(x,\xi)$ an *elementary solution* of (1) if

$$[\![\mathbf{L}_x h(x,\xi) = \delta(x-\xi)]\!]. \tag{2}$$

Let $H(x,\xi)$ be the one-sided Green's function for $\mathbf{L}$. Let

$$h(x,\xi) = H(x,\xi), \qquad x > \xi$$
$$h(x,\xi) = 0, \qquad x < \xi$$

or we may write

$$h(x,\xi) = H(x,\xi)\, u(x-\xi)$$

where $u(x-\xi)$ is the unit step function. We shall show that $h(x,\xi)$ is an elementary solution of $\mathbf{L}$.

From the properties of the Green's function,

$$H_k(\xi,\xi) = 0, \qquad 0 \leqq k \leqq n-2$$
$$H_{n-1}(\xi,\xi) = 1$$

where $H_k(x,\xi) = \partial^k H(x,\xi)/\partial x^k$. Now

$$h_k(x,\xi) = H_k(x,\xi)\, u(x-\xi), \qquad 0 \leqq k \leqq n-2,$$
$$[\![\, h_{n-1}(x,\xi) = \hat{H}_{n-1}(x,\xi)\, u(x-\xi) \,]\!]$$

and from (7.6)

$$[\![\, h_n(x,\xi) = \hat{H}_n(x,\xi)\, u(x-\xi) + 1\cdot\delta(x-\xi) \,]\!].$$

Since $H_k(x,\xi) = \hat{H}_k(x,\xi)$, $0 \leqq k \leqq n$, we have

$$[\![\, \mathbf{L}_x h(x,\xi) = [\mathbf{L}_x H(x,\xi)]\, u(x-\xi) + \delta(x-\xi) \,]\!]. \tag{3}$$

But $\hat{\mathbf{L}}_x H(x,\xi) = \mathbf{L}_x H(x,\xi) = 0$. Thus (3) reduces to (2).

6

THE CLASSICAL GREEN'S FUNCTION

1. Two-point Boundary Conditions

In preceding chapters we showed how to solve the linear differential equation

$$\mathbf{L}y = f(x) \tag{1}$$

together with the boundary conditions

$$y^{(j-1)}(x_0) = c_j, \qquad 1 \leqq j \leqq n. \tag{2}$$

As usual,

$$\mathbf{L} = p_0(x)\frac{d^n}{dx^n} + p_1(x)\frac{d^{n-1}}{dx^{n-1}} + \cdots + p_n(x)\cdot \tag{3}$$

is a linear differential operator of the nth order whose coefficients $p_i(x)$, $0 \leqq i \leqq n$, are continuous on some closed finite interval I, $p_0(x) > 0$ on I and x_0 is some point in I. Also we assumed $f(x) \in C^0(I)$; and the c_j, $1 \leqq j \leqq n$, are arbitrary constants.

A differential equation (1) together with a set of boundary conditions (2) is called a *differential system.* Thus if $H(x,\xi)$ is the one-sided Green's function for $\mathbf{L}$ and $\{\varphi_j(x)|1 \leqq j \leqq n\}$ is a fundamental set of solutions of $\mathbf{L}y = 0$ with the property that

$$\varphi_j^{(k-1)}(x_0) = \delta_{jk}, \qquad 1 \leqq j, k \leqq n,$$

then

$$y(x) = \sum_{j=1}^{n} c_j \, \varphi_j(x) + \int_{x_0}^{x} H(x,\xi) \, f(\xi) \, d\xi$$

is the unique solution of the differential system composed of (1) and (2).

We shall now consider more general differential systems. Let $\mathbf{L}$ be as defined by (3) and let

$$U_i(y) = \sum_{j=1}^{n} a_{ij} \, y^{(j-1)}(a) + \sum_{j=1}^{n} b_{ij} \, y^{(j-1)}(b), \qquad 1 \leqq i \leqq m, \tag{4}$$

where the a_{ij} and b_{ij} are constants, and a and b are any two distinct points in I. Then

$$\mathbf{L}y = f(x), \qquad f(x) \in C^0(I) \tag{5}$$

together with the supplementary conditions

$$U_i(y) = c_i, \qquad 1 \leqq i \leqq m, \tag{6}$$

constitute a differential system. Equations (1) and (2) form a special case of (5) and (6).

Boundary conditions such as (4) are called *two-point boundary conditions*, provided not all the a_{ij} and not all the b_{ij} are zero. Systems of the form

$$\begin{aligned} \mathbf{L}y &= f(x) \\ U_i(y) &= c_i, \qquad 1 \leqq i \leqq m, \end{aligned} \tag{7}$$

give rise to *two-point boundary value problems*. Such boundary value problems are of great mathematical interest. In fact they form the basis for the considerations in this and the next chapter. We shall therefore devote the remainder of this section to a discussion of the properties of two-point boundary conditions. In future sections we shall discuss the Green's functions appropriate to such boundary value problems.

If we let

$$Y_{2n}(y) = \{y(a), y'(a), \cdots, y^{(n-1)}(a), y(b), y'(b), \cdots, y^{(n-1)}(b)\} \tag{8}$$

be a $2n$-dimensional column vector and

$$P_{m,2n} = \| \, A_{mn} \, \vdots \, B_{mn} \, \|$$

be an $m \times 2n$ partitioned matrix where

$$A_{mn} = \|a_{ij}\|_{1 \leqq i \leqq m, 1 \leqq j \leqq n},$$
$$B_{mn} = \|b_{ij}\|_{1 \leqq i \leqq m, 1 \leqq j \leqq n},$$

then (4) may be written as

$$\mathbf{U}_m(y) = P_{m,2n}\, Y_{2n}(y) \tag{9}$$

where

$$\mathbf{U}_m(y) = \{U_1(y), U_2(y), \cdots, U_m(y)\} \tag{10}$$

is an m-dimensional vector.

The rank of $P_{m,2n}$ can be at most $2n$. That is, there can be at most $2n$ linearly independent boundary conditions of the form $U_i(y)$. Hence we may assume without loss of generality that $m \leqq 2n$. The problem that immediately arises is that of determining under what conditions (7) has a solution. Intimately associated with (7) is the completely homogeneous system

$$\begin{aligned} \mathbf{L}y &= 0 \\ U_i(y) &= 0, \qquad 1 \leqq i \leqq m, \end{aligned} \tag{11}$$

known as the *reduced system.* We shall examine first the reduced system.

If (11) has no solution not identically zero, we say "the completely homogeneous system is *incompatible*." If (11) has $p \leqq n$ linearly independent solutions, we call the system p-*ply compatible*, and call p the *index* of compatibility.

Suppose now that $\{\varphi_j(x) | 1 \leqq j \leqq n\}$ is a fundamental set of solutions of $\mathbf{L}y = 0$. Then

$$\varphi(x) = \sum_{j=1}^{n} \alpha_j \varphi_j(x)$$

satisfies $\mathbf{L}y = 0$. To satisfy the boundary conditions of (11) we must have

$$\sum_{j=1}^{n} \alpha_j\, U_i(\varphi_j) = 0, \qquad 1 \leqq i \leqq m. \tag{12}$$

We can consider (12) as a system of linear algebraic equations on the α_j. If the rank of the matrix

$$\mathscr{U}_{mn} = \|U_i(\varphi_j)\|_{1 \leqq i \leqq m, 1 \leqq j \leqq n} \tag{13}$$

is $n-p$, then p of the α_j may be chosen at will and the rest will be uniquely determined. Thus the system is p-ply compatible. Hence the rank of the matrix $\mathscr{U}_{mn}$ determines the index of compatibility of the linear differential system.

Theorem 1. Let

$$\begin{aligned} \mathbf{L}y &= 0 \\ U_i(y) &= 0, \qquad 1 \leqq i \leqq m, \end{aligned} \tag{14}$$

be a completely homogeneous linear differential system. Let

$$U_i(y) = \sum_{j=1}^{n} a_{ij} y^{(j-1)}(a) + \sum_{j=1}^{n} b_{ij} y^{(j-1)}(b), \qquad 1 \leqq i \leqq m,$$

and let $\{\varphi_j(x) | 1 \leqq j \leqq n\}$ be a fundamental system for $\mathbf{L}y=0$. Then a necessary and sufficient condition that the system (14) be p-ply compatible is that the rank of the matrix $\mathscr{U}_{mn} = \| U_i(\varphi_j) \|_{1 \leqq i \leqq m, 1 \leqq j \leqq n}$ be $n-p$.

Corollary. If the rank of $\mathscr{U}_{mn}$ is n, the completely homogeneous system is incompatible.

Consider now the non-homogeneous system

$$\mathbf{L}y = f(x), \qquad f(x) \in C^0(I) \tag{15a}$$

$$U_i(y) = c_i, \qquad 1 \leqq i \leqq m, \tag{15b}$$

corresponding to (14). Let $\mathbf{L}\psi(x) = f(x)$. Then

$$\varphi(x) = \psi(x) + \sum_{j=1}^{n} \alpha_j \varphi_j(x)$$

(where the α_j are arbitrary constants and $\mathbf{L}\varphi_j = 0$) satisfies (15a). To satisfy (15b) we must have

$$\sum_{j=1}^{n} \alpha_j U_i(\varphi_j) = c_i - U_i(\psi), \qquad 1 \leqq i \leqq m.$$

This system of algebraic equations will have a solution if and only if the rank of the augmented matrix

$$\| \mathscr{U}_{mn} \vdots C_m \|$$

(where $C_m = \{c_1 - U_1(\psi),\ c_2 - U_2(\psi), \cdots, c_m - U_m(\psi)\}$ is a column vector) is equal to the rank of $\mathscr{U}_{mn}$. If $m \leqq n$, then the rank of $\mathscr{U}_{mn}$ and the augmented matrix are always equal.

From Green's formula [cf. (2.1.4) and (4.4.5)] we see that

$$\int_a^b [v(\xi)\,\mathbf{L}u(\xi) - u(\xi)\,\mathbf{L}^*v(\xi)]\,d\xi = \pi[u(\xi), v(\xi)]\Big|_a^b$$
$$= U_1(u)V_{2n}(v) + U_2(u)V_{2n-1}(v) + \cdots + U_{2n}(u)V_1(v) \tag{16}$$

where

$$\mathbf{U}_{2n}(y) = P_{2n}\, Y_{2n}(y) \tag{17}$$

[cf. (9) and (10)]. Also from Section 4 of Chapter 4, the U_i, $1 \leqq i \leqq 2n$, are linearly independent and det $P_{2n} \neq 0$. Furthermore, the V_i, $1 \leqq i \leqq 2n$, are uniquely determined.

Now let $U_i(y)$, $1 \leqq i \leqq m$, be linearly independent and consider the differential system

$$\begin{aligned} \mathbf{L}y &= 0 \\ U_i(y) &= 0, \qquad 1 \leqq i \leqq m. \end{aligned} \tag{18}$$

Then we may choose $2n-m$ linearly independent forms $U_i(y)$, $m+1 \leqq i \leqq 2n$, such that the $U_i(y)$, $1 \leqq i \leqq 2n$, are linearly independent. By (16) we can uniquely determine the V_i, $1 \leqq i \leqq 2n$. The linear differential system

$$\begin{aligned} \mathbf{L}^*z &= 0 \\ V_i(z) &= 0, \qquad 1 \leqq i \leqq 2n-m, \end{aligned} \tag{19}$$

is called the *adjoint system* of (18). Clearly the definition is reciprocal; that is, (18) is the adjoint system of (19). By Theorem 1, a necessary and sufficient condition that (19) be p^*-ply compatible is that the rank of the matrix

$$\mathscr{V}_{2n-m,n} = \|V_{2n-m+1-i}(\varphi_j^*)\|_{1 \leqq i \leqq 2n-m,\, 1 \leqq j \leqq n} \tag{20}$$

be $n-p^*$ where $\{\varphi_j^*(x) | 1 \leqq j \leqq n\}$ are a fundamental system for $\mathbf{L}^*z = 0$.

We now consider the important special case where $m = n$. Suppose then that

$$\mathbf{L}y = 0 \tag{21a}$$
$$U_i(y) = 0, \qquad 1 \leqq i \leqq n, \tag{21b}$$

is p-ply compatible. We shall show that the adjoint system

$$\begin{aligned} \mathbf{L}^* z &= 0 \\ V_i(z) &= 0, \qquad 1 \leqq i \leqq n, \end{aligned} \tag{22}$$

is also p-ply compatible.

Let $\{f_i(x) | 1 \leqq i \leqq p\}$ be p linearly independent solutions of the differential system (21). That is, we are assuming (21) is p-ply compatible. Let $\{\varphi_j^*(x) | 1 \leqq j \leqq n\}$ be n linearly independent solutions of $\mathbf{L}^* z = 0$. Then by (16)

$$\begin{aligned} 0 &\equiv \int_a^b [\varphi_j^*(\xi)\, \mathbf{L} f_i(\xi) - f_i(\xi)\, \mathbf{L}^* \varphi_j^*(\xi)]\, d\xi \\ &= U_1(f_i) V_{2n}(\varphi_j^*) + U_2(f_i) V_{2n-1}(\varphi_j^*) + \cdots + U_{2n}(f_i) V_1(\varphi_j^*) \qquad (23) \\ &= U_{n+1}(f_i) V_n(\varphi_j^*) + U_{n+2}(f_i) V_{n-1}(\varphi_j^*) + \cdots + U_{2n}(f_i) V_1(\varphi_j^*) \end{aligned}$$

for $1 \leqq i \leqq p$ and $1 \leqq j \leqq n$. Equation (23) follows since $\mathbf{L} f_i = 0$, $\mathbf{L}^* \varphi_j^* = 0$ and the $f_i(x)$, $1 \leqq i \leqq p$ satisfy the boundary conditions of (21b). Thus

$$\tilde{\mathscr{V}}_{nn} \mathbf{U}_n^*(f_i) = \mathbf{0}_n, \qquad 1 \leqq i \leqq p, \tag{24}$$

where $\mathscr{V}_{nn} = \| V_{n+1-i}(\varphi_j^*) \|_{1 \leqq i,j \leqq n}$, [cf. (20)],

$$\mathbf{U}_n^*(y) = \{U_{n+1}(y), U_{n+2}(y), \cdots, U_{2n}(y)\},$$

[cf. (10)], and $\mathbf{0}_n = \{0, 0, \cdots, 0\}$ is the n-dimensional zero vector.

Certainly $\mathbf{U}_n^*(f_i)$, $1 \leqq i \leqq p$, are solutions of (24). If we can show that the $\mathbf{U}_n^*(f_i)$ are linearly independent, then the rank of $\mathscr{V}_{nn}$ will be at most $n - p$. But by Theorem 1, the rank of $\mathscr{V}_{nn}$ determines the index of the adjoint system. Thus if p^* is the index of (21), we conclude that

$$n - p^* \leqq n - p$$

or

$$p^* \geqq p.$$

Since (21) and (22) are reciprocal—that is, (21) is the adjoint of (22)—we can interchange the roles of (21) and (22) and prove

$$p^* \leqq p.$$

These last two equations imply $p = p^*$.

It remains but to show that the $\mathbf{U}_n^*(f_i)$ vectors, $1 \leqq i \leqq p$, are linearly independent. Suppose the contrary. Then there must exist constants β_i, $1 \leqq i \leqq p$, not all zero, such that

$$\sum_{i=1}^{p} \beta_i \, \mathbf{U}_n^*(f_i) = \mathbf{0}_n. \tag{25}$$

We shall force a contradiction by showing that $\beta_i = 0$, $1 \leqq i \leqq p$.

Let

$$\psi(x) = \sum_{i=1}^{p} \beta_i f_i(x). \tag{26}$$

Then (25) implies

$$\mathbf{U}_n^*(\psi) = \mathbf{0}_n. \tag{27}$$

But

$$\mathbf{U}_n(\psi) = \mathbf{0}_n \tag{28}$$

where $\mathbf{U}_n(y) = \{U_1(y), U_2(y), \cdots, U_n(y)\}$ since by hypothesis the f_i are solutions of (21). Thus, since

$$\mathbf{U}_{2n} = \{\mathbf{U}_n, \mathbf{U}_n^*\} = \{U_1, U_2, \cdots, U_{2n}\}$$

we have from (27) and (28) that

$$\mathbf{U}_{2n}(\psi) = \mathbf{0}_{2n}. \tag{29}$$

Now we recall from (17) that

$$\mathbf{U}_{2n}(y) = P_{2n} \, Y_{2n}(y)$$

and $\det P_{2n} \neq 0$. Thus (29) implies $Y_{2n}(\psi) = \mathbf{0}_{2n}$ which in turn implies

$$\psi^{(k-1)}(a) = 0 = \psi^{(k-1)}(b), \qquad 1 \leqq k \leqq n.$$

Since $\mathbf{L}\psi = 0$ this implies $\psi(x) \equiv 0$ on I. But the $f_i(x)$ are linearly independent. Hence (26) implies $\beta_i = 0$, $1 \leqq i \leqq p$, a contradiction.

We have therefore proved:

Theorem 2. Let

$$\begin{aligned} \mathbf{L}y &= 0 \\ U_i(y) &= 0, \qquad 1 \leqq i \leqq n, \end{aligned} \tag{30}$$

where the $U_i(y)$ are linearly independent. Let

$$\begin{aligned} \mathbf{L}^*z &= 0 \\ V_i(z) &= 0, \qquad 1 \leqq i \leqq n, \end{aligned} \tag{31}$$

be the adjoint system. Then the index of compatibility of (30) is the same as the index of compatibility of the adjoint system (31).

2. The Green's Function

The one-sided Green's function developed in an earlier chapter is admirably adapted to the study of one-point boundary value problems. However, many interesting problems (for example, Sturm-Liouville theory, to be discussed in the next chapter) fall into the category of *two*-point boundary value problems. What we would like to do now is to construct a function that will be as useful in the two-point theory as the one-sided Green's function was in the one-point type boundary value problem. Such a function does indeed exist. We shall call it the *classical Green's function*, or (since it antedates the one-sided Green's function) simply the *Green's function.*

Consider now the differential equation

$$\mathbf{L}y = r(x) \tag{1}$$

where $\mathbf{L}$ is as in (1.3) together with boundary conditions of the two-point type at a and b. If $H(x,\xi)$ is the one-sided Green's function for $\mathbf{L}$, then if

$$y(x) = \int_{x_0}^{x} H(x,\xi)\, r(\xi)\, d\xi$$

we have $\mathbf{L}y = r$. If we wish to satisfy the boundary conditions at $x = a$, we would like x_0 to be a. But if we wish to satisfy the boundary conditions at b, we would like x_0 to be b. In other words, when we have two-point boundary conditions we would like $y(x)$ to behave like $\int_a^x H(x,\xi)r(\xi)\, d\xi$ near $x = a$, and to behave like $-\int_x^b H(x,\xi)r(\xi)\, d\xi$ near $x = b$. Let us therefore define $g(x,\xi)$ as

$$\begin{aligned} g(x,\xi) &= \tfrac{1}{2}H(x,\xi), \qquad \xi < x \\ g(x,\xi) &= -\tfrac{1}{2}H(x,\xi), \qquad \xi > x \end{aligned} \tag{2}$$

and investigate some of its properties. From Theorem 1 of Chapter 3 we recall that

$$\mathbf{L}_x H(x,\xi) = 0.$$

Hence

$$\mathbf{L}_x g(x,\xi) = \tfrac{1}{2}\mathbf{L}_x H(x,\xi) = 0, \qquad \xi < x$$
$$\mathbf{L}_x g(x,\xi) = \tfrac{1}{2}\mathbf{L}_x H(x,\xi) = 0, \qquad \xi > x$$

or

$$\hat{\mathbf{L}}_x g(x,\xi) = 0. \tag{3}$$

(Recall the definition of $\hat{\mathbf{L}}$, Section 8 of Chapter 5.)

We shall now show that if $r(x)$ is any function continuous on $[a,b]$, and

$$f(x) = \int_a^b g(x,\xi)\, r(\xi)\, d\xi, \tag{4}$$

then $\mathbf{L}f(x) = r(x)$. To do this most conveniently, write (2) as

$$g(x,\xi) = \tfrac{1}{2}H(x,\xi)\, u(x-\xi) - \tfrac{1}{2}H(x,\xi)\, u(\xi-x) \tag{5}$$

where u is the unit step function. Since $g(x,\xi)$ and its first $n-2$ derivatives vanish at $x=\xi$ (cf. Theorem 1 of Chapter 3), we may write

$$g_k(x,\xi) = \tfrac{1}{2}H_k(x,\xi)\, u(x-\xi) - \tfrac{1}{2}H_k(x,\xi)\, u(\xi-x), \qquad 0 \leqq k \leqq n-1, \tag{6}$$

where we are again using the abbreviated notations

$$g_k(x,\xi) = \frac{\partial^k}{\partial x^k}\, g(x,\xi), \qquad H_k(x,\xi) = \frac{\partial^k}{\partial x^k}\, H(x,\xi), \qquad 0 \leqq k \leqq n.$$

From (6)

$$[\![\; g_n(x,\xi) = \tfrac{1}{2}H_n(x,\xi)\, u(x-\xi) - \tfrac{1}{2}H_n(x,\xi)\, u(\xi-x)$$
$$+ \tfrac{1}{2}H_{n-1}(x,\xi)\, \delta(x-\xi) + \tfrac{1}{2}H_{n-1}(x,\xi)\, \delta(\xi-x) \;]\!]$$

or

$$[\![\; p_0(x)\, g_n(x,\xi) = p_0(x)\, \hat{g}_n(x,\xi) + p_0(x)\, H_{n-1}(x,\xi)\, \delta(x-\xi) \;]\!]$$

or

$$[\![\; p_0(x)\, g_n(x,\xi) = p_0(x)\, \hat{g}_n(x,\xi) + \delta(x-\xi) \;]\!]. \tag{7}$$

Thus (6) and (7) imply

$$\mathbf{L}_x f = \int_a^b \mathbf{L}_x g(x,\xi) r(\xi)\, d\xi = \int_a^b [\hat{\mathbf{L}}_x g(x,\xi) + \delta(x-\xi)] r(\xi)\, d\xi$$
$$= 0 + r(x)$$

by (3), and (4) is established.

Consider now the two-point boundary value problem

$$\begin{aligned} \mathbf{L}y &= r(x) \\ U_i(y) &= 0, \qquad 1 \leqq i \leqq n. \end{aligned} \tag{8}$$

We shall assume that $\mathbf{L}$ is an nth-order linear differential operator with continuous coefficients on some closed finite interval $I = [a,b]$, whose leading coefficient is positive on $[a,b]$. The $U_i(y)$ will be two-point boundary conditions of the form

$$U_i(y) = \sum_{j=1}^{n} a_{ij} y^{(j-1)}(a) + \sum_{j=1}^{n} b_{ij} y^{(j-1)}(b), \qquad 1 \leqq i \leqq n. \tag{9}$$

Furthermore, we shall assume that the completely homogeneous system

$$\begin{aligned} \mathbf{L}y &= 0 \\ U_i(y) &= 0, \qquad 1 \leqq i \leqq n, \end{aligned} \tag{10}$$

is incompatible.

Now let

$$G(x,\xi) = g(x,\xi) + \sum_{j=1}^{n} \psi_j(\xi)\, \varphi_j(x)$$

where $g(x,\xi)$ has been defined by (2) and the $\varphi_j(x)$, $1 \leqq j \leqq n$, form a fundamental system for $\mathbf{L}y = 0$. The $\psi_j(\xi)$ are yet to be determined. From the above analysis it is clear that if

$$f(x) = \int_a^b G(x,\xi)\, r(\xi)\, d\xi,$$

then

$$\mathbf{L}f = r(x).$$

Let us determine the $\psi_j(\xi)$, $1 \leqq j \leqq n$, such that $f(x)$ satisfies the two-point boundary conditions of (9). For this to be true we must have

$$U_i(f) = \int_a^b U_i(G)\, r(\xi)\, d\xi = 0$$

or

$$U_i(G) = 0, \qquad 1 \leqq i \leqq n.$$

It is understood that U_i acts on the variable x in $U_i(G)$. Hence

$$U_i(G) = 0 = U_i(g) + \sum_{j=1}^{n} \psi_j(\xi)\, U_i(\varphi_j)$$

or

$$\sum_{j=1}^{n} \psi_j(\xi)\, U_i(\varphi_j) = -U_i(g), \qquad 1 \leqq i \leqq n. \tag{11}$$

Since the rank of the matrix

$$\mathscr{U} = \| U_i(\varphi_j) \|_{1 \leqq i,j \leqq n}$$

is maximal, we may solve (11) for the $\psi_j(\xi)$ by Cramer's rule. Thus we may write

$$G(x,\xi) = \frac{1}{D(U)} \begin{vmatrix} g(x,\xi) & \varphi_1(x) & \varphi_2(x) & \cdots & \varphi_n(x) \\ U_1(g) & U_1(\varphi_1) & U_1(\varphi_2) & \cdots & U_1(\varphi_n) \\ U_2(g) & U_2(\varphi_1) & U_2(\varphi_2) & \cdots & U_2(\varphi_n) \\ \cdot & \cdot & \cdot & \cdot & \cdot \\ U_n(g) & U_n(\varphi_1) & U_n(\varphi_2) & \cdots & U_n(\varphi_n) \end{vmatrix} \tag{12}$$

$$= g(x,\xi) - \tilde{\Phi}(x)\, \mathscr{U}^{-1}\, \mathbf{U}(g)$$

where $D(U) = \det \mathscr{U}$, and $\Phi(x) = \{\varphi_1(x), \varphi_2(x), \cdots, \varphi_n(x)\}$ and $\mathbf{U}(y) = \{U_1(y), U_2(y), \cdots, U_n(y)\}$ are n-dimensional column vectors.

The function $G(x,\xi)$ defined by (12) is called the *classical Green's function* or simply the *Green's function* for the differential system of (10). The one-sided Green's function is associated with a differential *operator*; the classical Green's function is associated with a differential *system*.

As an immediate consequence of this definition and our previous discussion we see that the Green's function enjoys the following properties:

Theorem 3. Let $G(x,\xi)$ be the classical Green's function for the nth-order linear differential system of (10). Then

(i) $G(x,\xi)$ and $\dfrac{\partial^k}{\partial x^k} G(x,\xi)$, $1 \leqq k \leqq n-2$, are jointly continuous in x and ξ on the square $I \times I$.

(ii) $\left.\frac{\partial^{n-1}}{\partial x^{n-1}} G(x,\xi)\right|_{x=\xi+} - \left.\frac{\partial^{n-1}}{\partial x^{n-1}} G(x,\xi)\right|_{x=\xi-} = \frac{1}{p_0(\xi)}.$

(iii) $\hat{\mathbf{L}}_x\, G(x,\xi) = 0.$

(iv) $U_i(G) = 0, \qquad 1 \leqq i \leqq n.$

We leave the proof to the reader.

The Green's function is unique in the following sense:

Theorem 4. Let $G(x,\xi)$ be as defined by (12). Let $K(x,\xi)$ be any function jointly continuous on $I \times I$ with the property that

$$y(x) = \int_a^b K(x,\xi)\, r(\xi)\, d\xi$$

is a solution of the non-homogeneous equation $\mathbf{L}y = r(x)$ for every $r(x)$ continuous on I, and satisfies the incompatible boundary conditions

$$U_i(y) = 0, \qquad 1 \leqq i \leqq n.$$

Then $K(x,\xi) \equiv G(x,\xi)$ on $I \times I$.

Proof. Same as Theorem 3 of Chapter 3.

3. Green's Function of the Adjoint System

We now turn to a consideration of the relation of the Green's function of a linear differential system to the Green's function of the adjoint system. Let

$$\mathbf{L} = p_0(x)\frac{d^n}{dx^n} + p_1(x)\frac{d^{n-1}}{dx^{n-1}} + \cdots + p_n(x)\cdot \tag{1}$$

where the $p_i(x) \in C^{n-i}(I)$ and $p_0(x) > 0$ on the closed finite interval $I = [a,b]$. Let $\mathbf{L}^*$ be the adjoint operator. Let $U_i(y)$, $1 \leqq i \leqq n$, be any n linearly independent forms [cf. (2.9)]. Then the differential system

$$\begin{aligned} \mathbf{L}y &= 0 \\ U_i(y) &= 0, \qquad 1 \leqq i \leqq n, \end{aligned} \tag{2}$$

is incompatible. Now choose any n additional forms $U_i(y)$, $n+1 \leqq$

$i \leqq 2n$, such that the $2n$ forms $U_i(y)$, $1 \leqq i \leqq 2n$, are independent. Then there exist $2n$ unique, linearly independent forms $U_i^*(z)$, $1 \leqq i \leqq 2n$, such that

$$\int_a^b [v(\xi)\,\mathbf{L}u(\xi) - u(\xi)\,\mathbf{L}^*v(\xi)]\,d\xi$$
$$= U_1(u)U_{2n}^*(v) + U_2(u)U_{2n-1}^*(v) + \cdots + U_{2n}(u)U_1^*(v) \tag{3}$$

[where $u(x), v(x) \in C^n(I)$]. We recall that

$$\begin{aligned} \mathbf{L}^*y^* &= 0 \\ U_i^*(y^*) &= 0, \qquad 1 \leqq i \leqq n, \end{aligned} \tag{4}$$

is called the system adjoint to (2). Furthermore, if (2) is incompatible, so is the reduced system of (4). We also recall from Section 4 of Chapter 4 that if any other forms $\bar{U}_i(y)$, $n+1 \leqq i \leqq 2n$, are chosen so that the $2n$ forms

$$U_1(y), U_2(y), \cdots, U_n(y), \bar{U}_{n+1}(y), \bar{U}_{n+2}(y), \cdots, \bar{U}_{2n}(y)$$

are linearly independent, then

$$\int_a^b (v\,\mathbf{L}u - u\,\mathbf{L}^*v)\,d\xi = U_1(u)\bar{U}_{2n}^*(v) + U_2(u)\bar{U}_{2n-1}^*(v) + \cdots$$
$$+ U_n(u)\bar{U}_{n+1}^*(v) + \bar{U}_{n+1}(u)\bar{U}_n^*(v) + \cdots + \bar{U}_{2n}(u)\bar{U}_1^*(v)$$

where $\bar{U}_1^*, \bar{U}_2^*, \cdots, \bar{U}_n^*$ are simply linear combinations of $U_1^*, U_2^*, \cdots, U_n^*$ only. In other words, the choice of U_i^*, $1 \leqq i \leqq n$, depends only on the choice of U_i, $1 \leqq i \leqq n$.

We shall now show that if $G(x,\xi)$ is the Green's function of the system (2) and $G^*(x,\xi)$ is the Green's function for the adjoint system of (4), then

$$G(x,\xi) = G^*(\xi,x).$$

To prove this we use Green's formula to write

$$\int_a^b [G^*(x,\zeta)\,\mathbf{L}_x G(x,\xi) - G(x,\xi)\,\mathbf{L}_x^* G^*(x,\zeta)]\,dx$$
$$= \sum_{i=1}^{2n} U_i(G)\,U_{2n+1-i}^*(G^*).$$

But $U_i(G) = 0 = U_i^*(G^*)$, $1 \leqq i \leqq n$. Hence

$$\int_a^b [G^*(x,\zeta)\, \mathbf{L}_x G(x,\xi) - G(x,\xi)\, \mathbf{L}_x^* G^*(x,\zeta)]\, dx = 0. \tag{5}$$

But we also have

$$\begin{aligned} &\int_a^b [G^*(x,\zeta)\, \mathbf{L}_x G(x,\xi) - G(x,\xi)\, \mathbf{L}_x^* G^*(x,\zeta)]\, dx \\ &= \int_a^b \{G^*(x,\zeta)\, [\hat{\mathbf{L}}_x G(x,\xi) + \delta(x-\xi)] \\ &\qquad - G(x,\xi)\, [\hat{\mathbf{L}}_x^* G^*(x,\zeta) + \delta(x-\zeta)]\}\, dx. \end{aligned} \tag{6}$$

Since

$$\hat{\mathbf{L}}_x G(x,\xi) = 0 = \hat{\mathbf{L}}_x^* G^*(x,\zeta)$$

we infer from (5) and (6) that

$$G^*(\xi,\zeta) = G(\zeta,\xi). \tag{7}$$

Thus we have proved the following theorem:

Theorem 5. Let

$$\mathbf{L} = p_0(x)\, \frac{d^n}{dx^n} + p_1(x)\, \frac{d^{n-1}}{dx^{n-1}} + \cdots + p_n(x)\cdot$$

where the $p_i(x)$ are of class C^{n-i}, $0 \leqq i \leqq n$, on some closed finite interval I and $p_0(x) > 0$ on I. Let the completely homogeneous system

$$\mathbf{L}y = 0$$
$$U_i(y) = 0, \qquad 1 \leqq i \leqq n,$$

where the $U_i(y)$ are two-point boundary conditions, be incompatible. Let

$$\mathbf{L}^* y^* = 0$$
$$U_i^*(y^*) = 0, \qquad 1 \leqq i \leqq n,$$

be the (also incompatible) adjoint system. Let $G(x,\xi)$ and $G^*(x,\xi)$ be the Green's functions, respectively, of these two systems. Then for every (x,ξ) in $I \times I$,

$$G^*(\xi,x) = G(x,\xi).$$

4. Further Properties of the Green's Function

In Theorem 6 of Chapter 3 we showed how a fundamental set of solutions of a linear differential operator could be explicitly constructed from the one-sided Green's function. The same state of affairs exists with regard to the classical Green's function. We prove this important result in the next theorem.

Theorem 6. Let

$$\mathbf{L} = p_0(x)\frac{d^n}{dx^n} + p_1(x)\frac{d^{n-1}}{dx^{n-1}} + \cdots + p_n(x)\cdot$$

where the $p_i(x)$ are of class C^{n-i}, $0 \leqq i \leqq n$, on some closed finite interval $I = [a,b]$ and $p_0(x) > 0$ on I. Let $U_i(y)$, $1 \leqq i \leqq n$, be two-point boundary conditions such that the completely homogeneous differential system

$$\mathbf{L}y = 0$$
$$U_i(y) = 0, \qquad 1 \leqq i \leqq n,$$

is incompatible. Let $G(x,\xi)$ be the Green's function for this system. Let

$$\begin{aligned} \mathbf{L}^*y^* &= 0 \\ U_i^*(y^*) &= 0, \qquad 1 \leqq i \leqq n, \end{aligned} \tag{1}$$

be the (necessarily incompatible) adjoint system. Let $\mathbf{V}_n(z) = \{U_1^*(z), U_2^*(z), \cdots, U_n^*(z)\}$ and $Z_{2n}(z) = \{z(a), z'(a), \cdots, z^{(n-1)}(a), z(b), z'(b), \cdots, z^{(n-1)}(b)\}$ be column vectors and let

$$\mathbf{V}_n(z) = C_{n,2n}\, Z_{2n}(z)$$

where $C_{n,2n} = \|c_{ij}\|_{1\leqq i\leqq n, 1\leqq j\leqq 2n}$ is an $n \times 2n$ matrix of rank n. Let $\|c_{ij_\beta}\|_{1\leqq i,\beta\leqq n}$ be a non-singular submatrix of $C_{n,2n}$. Let

$$\psi_k(x) = \frac{\partial^{k-1}}{\partial\xi^{k-1}} G(x,\xi)\bigg|_{\xi=a}, \quad \psi_{n+k}(x) = \frac{\partial^{k-1}}{\partial\xi^{k-1}} G(x,\xi)\bigg|_{\xi=b}, \quad 1 \leqq k \leqq n.$$

Then the n functions $\{\psi_{j_{n+\beta}}(x) | 1 \leqq \beta \leqq n\}$ form a fundamental set of solutions of $\mathbf{L}y = 0$.

Proof. Certainly $\mathbf{L}\psi_\beta(x) = 0$, $1 \leqq \beta \leqq 2n$, and there are at most n linearly independent solutions of $\mathbf{L}y = 0$. We shall show that there are at least (and hence exactly) n linearly independent functions among the $\psi_\beta(x)$, $1 \leqq \beta \leqq 2n$. Let $\varphi(x)$ be *any* solution of $\mathbf{L}y=0$. Then by Green's formula

$$\int_a^b [G^*(x,\xi)\,\mathbf{L}\varphi(x) - \varphi(x)\,\mathbf{L}_x^* G^*(x,\xi)]\,dx$$

$$= -\int_a^b \varphi(x)[\hat{\mathbf{L}}_x^* G^*(x,\xi) + \delta(x-\xi)]\,dx = -\varphi(\xi) \tag{2}$$

$$= U_1(\varphi)U_{2n}^*(G^*) + U_2(\varphi)U_{2n-1}^*(G^*) + \cdots + U_{2n}(\varphi)U_1^*(G^*)$$

$$= U_1(\varphi)U_{2n}^*(G^*) + U_2(\varphi)U_{2n-1}^*(G^*) + \cdots + U_n(\varphi)U_{n+1}^*(G^*)$$

since $U_i^*(G^*) = 0$, $1 \leqq i \leqq n$, where G^* is the Green's function for the adjoint system (1).

Now $U_{n+1}^*(G^*)$, $U_{n+2}^*(G^*)$, $\cdots$, $U_{2n}^*(G^*)$ are linear combinations of the $\psi_\beta(\xi)$ and the $U_1(\varphi)$, $U_2(\varphi)$, $\cdots$, $U_n(\varphi)$ are constants. Thus

$$\varphi(x) = \sum_{k=1}^{2n} a_k\, \psi_k(\xi).$$

Since φ is an arbitrary solution of $\mathbf{L}y=0$, there must exist at least n linearly independent solutions of $\mathbf{L}y=0$ among the $\psi_k(\xi)$, $1 \leqq k \leqq 2n$.

The rank of $C_{n,2n}$ is n since the $U_i^*(y)$ are linearly independent and

$$\mathbf{0}_n = \mathbf{V}_n(G^*) = C_{n,2n}\, Z_{2n}(G^*) = C_{n,2n}\, Z_{2n}(\psi)$$

where

$$Z_{2n}(\psi) = \{\psi_1, \psi_2, \cdots, \psi_{2n}\}$$

and $\mathbf{0}_n = \{0, 0, \cdots, 0\}$ is the n-dimensional zero vector. Let $|c_{i,j_\beta}|_{1 \leqq i,\beta \leqq n}$ be a non-singular submatrix of $C_{n,2n}$. Then every $\psi_k(x)$, $1 \leqq k \leqq 2n$, can be expressed as a linear combination of the $\psi_{j_{n+\beta}}(x)$, $1 \leqq \beta \leqq n$. Hence $\{\psi_{j_{n+\beta}}(x) | 1 \leqq \beta \leqq n\}$ form a fundamental set of solutions of $\mathbf{L}y=0$.

If the nth-order linear differential operator $\mathbf{L}$ is formally self-adjoint, that is $\mathbf{L} = (-1)^n\mathbf{L}^*$, then we have seen that

$$H(x,\xi) = (-1)^{n+1}\, H(\xi,x)$$

where $H(x,\xi)$ is the one-sided Green's function for $\mathbf{L}$. We shall show that

$$G(x,\xi) = (-1)^n G(\xi,x)$$

for a self-adjoint differential system.

Let

$$\begin{aligned} \mathbf{L}y &= 0 \\ U_i(y) &= 0, \qquad 1 \leqq i \leqq n, \end{aligned} \tag{3}$$

be an incompatible linear differential system of the nth order and

$$\begin{aligned} \mathbf{L}^*y^* &= 0 \\ U_i^*(y^*) &= 0, \qquad 1 \leqq i \leqq n, \end{aligned} \tag{4}$$

the adjoint system. We say (3) is *self-adjoint* if $\mathbf{L}$ is formally self-adjoint and the U_i are linear combinations of U_i^*, and conversely. The classical Green's function $G(x,\xi)$ for (3) is given by (2.12); and $G^*(x,\xi)$, the Green's function for (4), is given by

$$G^*(x,\xi) = \frac{1}{D(U^*)}\begin{vmatrix} g^*(x,\xi) & \varphi_1^*(x) & \varphi_2^*(x) & \cdots & \varphi_n^*(x) \\ U_1^*(g^*) & U_1^*(\varphi_1^*) & U_1^*(\varphi_2^*) & \cdots & U_1^*(\varphi_n^*) \\ U_2^*(g^*) & U_2^*(\varphi_1^*) & U_2^*(\varphi_2^*) & \cdots & U_2^*(\varphi_n^*) \\ \cdot & \cdot & \cdot & \cdot & \cdot \\ U_n^*(g^*) & U_n^*(\varphi_1^*) & U_n^*(\varphi_2^*) & \cdots & U_n^*(\varphi_n^*) \end{vmatrix} \tag{5}$$

where $\{\varphi_j^*(x) | 1 \leqq j \leqq n\}$ form a fundamental set of solutions of $\mathbf{L}^*z = 0$, $D(U^*) = \det \| U_i^*(\varphi_j^*) \|_{1 \leqq i,j \leqq n}$, and

$$\begin{aligned} g^*(x,\xi) &= \tfrac{1}{2}H^*(x,\xi), \qquad & \xi < x \\ g^*(x,\xi) &= -\tfrac{1}{2}H^*(x,\xi), \qquad & \xi > x \end{aligned}$$

where $H^*(x,\xi)$ is the one-sided Green's function for $\mathbf{L}^*$.

Since the U_i^* are linear combinations of the U_i, $1 \leqq i \leqq n$, and conversely, and since $\{\varphi_j(x) | 1 \leqq j \leqq n\}$ is a fundamental system for $\mathbf{L}^*z = 0$, we may write without loss of generality (by the uniqueness of the Green's function) that

$$G^*(x,\xi) = \frac{1}{D(U)}\begin{vmatrix} g^*(x,\xi) & \varphi_1(x) & \varphi_2(x) & \cdots & \varphi_n(x) \\ U_1(g^*) & U_1(\varphi_1) & U_1(\varphi_2) & \cdots & U_1(\varphi_n) \\ \cdot & \cdot & \cdot & \cdot & \cdot \\ U_n(g^*) & U_n(\varphi_1) & U_n(\varphi_2) & \cdots & U_n(\varphi_n) \end{vmatrix}. \tag{6}$$

But $g^*(x,\xi) = g(\xi,x)$; and since $\mathbf{L}$ is self-adjoint, $g(x,\xi) = (-1)^n g(\xi,x)$. Hence

$$g^*(x,\xi) = (-1)^n\, g(x,\xi).$$

Using this result in (6) and comparing with (2.12), we conclude that

$$G(x,\xi) = (-1)^n\, G(\xi,x).$$

Hence we have shown:

Theorem 7. If $G(x,\xi)$ is the Green's function for the nth-order, self-adjoint, incompatible linear differential system

$$\mathbf{L}y = 0$$
$$U_i(y) = 0, \qquad 1 \leqq i \leqq n,$$

then

$$G(x,\xi) = (-1)^n\, G(\xi,x).$$

Another criterion for self-adjointness analogous to that developed in Section 3 of Chapter 4 for the one-sided Green's function can also be derived. As usual let

$$\mathbf{L} = p_0(x)\frac{d^n}{dx^n} + p_1(x)\frac{d^{n-1}}{dx^{n-1}} + \cdots + p_n(x)\cdot$$

where the $p_i(x)$ are of class C^{n-i}, $0 \leqq i \leqq n$, on some closed finite interval $I = [a,b]$ and $p_0(x) > 0$ on I. Let

$$U_i(y) = A_i(y) + B_i(y), \qquad 1 \leqq i \leqq n,$$

where

$$A_i(y) = \sum_{j=1}^{n} a_{ij}\, y^{(j-1)}(a), \qquad 1 \leqq i \leqq n,$$

and

$$B_i(y) = \sum_{j=1}^{n} b_{ij}\, y^{(j-1)}(b), \qquad 1 \leqq i \leqq n,$$

be so chosen that the completely homogeneous system

$$\begin{aligned} \mathbf{L}y &= 0 \\ U_i(y) &= 0, \qquad 1 \leqq i \leqq n, \end{aligned} \tag{7}$$

is incompatible. Let

$$V_i(y) = A_i(y) - B_i(y), \qquad 1 \leqq i \leqq n,$$

and define the two matrices $\mathscr{U}$ and $\mathscr{V}$ as

$$\mathscr{U} = \|U_i(\varphi_j)\|_{1 \leqq i,j \leqq n}, \qquad \mathscr{V} = \|V_i(\varphi_j)\|_{1 \leqq i,j \leqq n}$$

where $\{\varphi_j(x) | 1 \leqq j \leqq n\}$ form a fundamental system of solutions for $\mathbf{L}y = 0$.

We recall from Section 3 of Chapter 4 that the one-sided Green's function $H(x,\xi)$ of $\mathbf{L}$ may be written

$$H(x,\xi) = \tilde{\Phi}(x) \; C \; \Phi(\xi)$$

where $\Phi(x) = \{\varphi_1(x), \varphi_2(x), \cdots, \varphi_n(x)\}$ is a column vector of fundamental solutions of $\mathbf{L}y = 0$ and $\tilde{\Phi}(x)$ is its transpose. Furthermore, we showed that

$$\tilde{C} = (-1)^{n+1} \; C. \tag{8}$$

We shall now prove the following result:

Theorem 8. If the differential system of (7) is self-adjoint, then $\mathscr{V} C \tilde{\mathscr{U}}$ is symmetric if n is even and $\mathscr{V} C \tilde{\mathscr{U}}$ is skew-symmetric if n is odd.

Proof. From (2.12) we may write

$$G(x,\xi) = g(x,\xi) - \tilde{\Phi}(x) \; \mathscr{U}^{-1} \; \mathbf{U}(g)$$

where $\mathbf{U}(g) = \{U_1(g), U_2(g), \cdots, U_n(g)\}$. From (2.2)

$$g(x,\xi) = \tfrac{1}{2} \operatorname{sgn}(x - \xi) \; H(x,\xi)$$

where $H(x,\xi)$ is the one-sided Green's function for $\mathbf{L}$ and

$$\operatorname{sgn}(x-\xi) = +1, \qquad x > \xi$$

$$\operatorname{sgn}(x-\xi) = -1, \qquad x < \xi.$$

Thus

$$\begin{aligned} U_i(g) &= \tfrac{1}{2} \; U_i(\operatorname{sgn}(x-\xi) \; \tilde{\Phi}(x)) \; C \; \Phi(\xi), \qquad 1 \leqq i \leqq n, \\ &= -\tfrac{1}{2} \; V_i(\tilde{\Phi}(x)) \; C \; \Phi(\xi) \end{aligned}$$

and

$$\mathbf{U}(g) = -\tfrac{1}{2} \mathscr{V} C \; \Phi(\xi).$$

Hence

$$\begin{aligned} G(x,\xi) &= g(x,\xi) + \tfrac{1}{2} \; \tilde{\Phi}(x) \mathscr{U}^{-1} \mathscr{V} C \; \Phi(\xi) \\ &= g(x,\xi) + \tfrac{1}{2} \; \tilde{\Phi}(\xi) \; \tilde{C} \tilde{\mathscr{V}} \tilde{\mathscr{U}}^{-1} \; \Phi(x) \end{aligned}$$

since $\tilde{\Phi}\,\mathscr{U}^{-1}\mathscr{V}C\,\Phi$ is a scalar. But from Theorem 7

$$G(x,\xi) = (-1)^n\, G(\xi,x)$$

and $g(x,\xi) = (-1)^n\, g(\xi,x)$. Hence

$$\tilde{\Phi}(\xi)\,\tilde{C}\tilde{\mathscr{V}}\tilde{\mathscr{U}}^{-1}\,\Phi(x) = (-1)^n\,\tilde{\Phi}(\xi)\mathscr{U}^{-1}\mathscr{V}C\,\Phi(x)$$

or

$$\tilde{C}\tilde{\mathscr{V}}\tilde{\mathscr{U}}^{-1} = (-1)^n\mathscr{U}^{-1}\mathscr{V}C.$$

Thus

$$\mathscr{U}\tilde{C}\tilde{\mathscr{V}} = (-1)^n\mathscr{V}C\tilde{\mathscr{U}} = (-1)^n\widetilde{(\mathscr{U}\tilde{C}\tilde{\mathscr{V}})}$$

as was desired to be proved.

Using (8) we may also write

$$\mathscr{U}C\tilde{\mathscr{V}} = -\mathscr{V}C\tilde{\mathscr{U}}. \tag{9}$$

If $\mathbf{L}$ and $\mathbf{M}$ are linear differential operators, we have shown in Theorem 7 of Chapter 3 that the one-sided Green's function of the composition $\mathbf{LM}$ is essentially the convolution of the one-sided Green's functions of $\mathbf{L}$ and $\mathbf{M}$. The corresponding result (Tricomi's theorem) for the classical Green's function is given in Theorem 9 below.

Theorem 9. Let

$$\mathbf{L} = p_0(x)\frac{d^n}{dx^n} + p_1(x)\frac{d^{n-1}}{dx^{n-1}} + \cdots + p_n(x)\cdot$$

be a linear differential operator whose coefficients are continuous on the closed finite interval $I=[a,b]$ and $p_0(x) > 0$ on I. Let

$$U_i(y) = \sum_{j=1}^{n} a_{ij}\, y^{(j-1)}(a) + \sum_{j=1}^{n} b_{ij}\, y^{(j-1)}(b), \qquad 1 \leqq i \leqq n,$$

be two-point boundary conditions so chosen that the completely homogeneous system

$$\begin{aligned} \mathbf{L}y &= 0 \\ U_i(y) &= 0, \qquad 1 \leqq i \leqq n, \end{aligned} \tag{10}$$

is incompatible. Let

$$\mathbf{M} = q_0(x)\frac{d^m}{dx^m} + q_1(x)\frac{d^{m-1}}{dx^{m-1}} + \cdots + q_m(x).$$

be a linear differential operator where the coefficients are of class $C^n(I)$ and $q_0(x) > 0$ on I. Let

$$V_i(y) = \sum_{j=1}^{m} \alpha_{ij}\, y^{(j-1)}(a) + \sum_{j=1}^{m} \beta_{ij}\, y^{(j-1)}(b), \qquad 1 \leqq i \leqq m,$$

be two-point boundary conditions so chosen that the completely homogeneous system

$$\begin{aligned} \mathbf{M}z &= 0 \\ V_i(z) &= 0, \qquad 1 \leqq i \leqq m, \end{aligned} \tag{11}$$

is incompatible. Let $G_L(x,\xi)$ and $G_M(x,\xi)$ be the Green's functions of (10) and (11) respectively. Then

$$G_{LM}(x,\xi) = \int_a^b G_M(x,\zeta)\, G_L(\zeta,\xi)\, d\zeta$$

is the Green's function for the linear differential system

$$\begin{aligned} \mathbf{LM}u &= 0 \\ U_i(\mathbf{M}u) &= 0, \qquad 1 \leqq i \leqq n, \\ V_i(u) &= 0, \qquad 1 \leqq i \leqq m. \end{aligned}$$

Proof. Let $f(x) \in C^0(I)$ and define $w(x)$ as the solution of the differentiable system

$$\begin{aligned} \mathbf{L}w(x) &= f(x) \\ U_i(w) &= 0, \qquad 1 \leqq i \leqq n. \end{aligned} \tag{12}$$

Define $u(x)$ as the solution of the differential system

$$\begin{aligned} \mathbf{M}u(x) &= w(x) \\ V_i(u) &= 0, \qquad 1 \leqq i \leqq m. \end{aligned} \tag{13}$$

From (12) follows

$$w(\zeta) = \int_a^b G_L(\zeta,\xi)\, f(\xi)\, d\xi \tag{14}$$

and

$$U_i(w) = 0, \qquad 1 \leqq i \leqq n. \tag{15}$$

From (13) follows

$$u(x) = \int_a^b G_M(x,\zeta)\, w(\zeta)\, d\zeta \tag{16}$$

and

$$V_i(u) = 0, \qquad 1 \leqq i \leqq m. \tag{17}$$

Now substitute (14) in (16):

$$u(x) = \int_a^b G_M(x,\zeta) \int_a^b G_L(\zeta,\xi)\, f(\xi)\, d\xi\, d\zeta$$

$$= \int_a^b \left[\int_a^b G_M(x,\zeta)\, G_L(\zeta,\xi)\, d\zeta \right] f(\xi)\, d\xi$$

while from (15) and (17) follows

$$U_i(w) = U_i(\mathbf{M}u) = 0, \qquad 1 \leqq i \leqq n,$$
$$V_i(u) = 0, \qquad 1 \leqq i \leqq m.$$

But from (12) and (13)

$$f(x) = \mathbf{L}w(x) = \mathbf{L}(\mathbf{M}u) = (\mathbf{LM})u(x)$$

—which proves our theorem.

7
STURM-LIOUVILLE THEORY

1. The Fundamental Problems

Sturm-Liouville theory is centered about the study of second order self-adjoint linear differential systems depending on a parameter, λ. Let

$$\mathbf{L}y = 0 \tag{1a}$$

$$\left.\begin{aligned} U_1(y) &= 0 \\ U_2(y) &= 0 \end{aligned}\right. \tag{1b}$$

be a second order self-adjoint system. Some of the objectives of the theory are:

(1) Find those values of λ for which (1a) has a non-identically zero solution satisfying (1b).

(2) If $\varphi_n(x)$ is the solution of (1) corresponding to $\lambda = \lambda_n$, under what conditions can we express an arbitrary function $f(x)$ in the form

$$f(x) = \sum_{n=0}^{\infty} c_n \varphi_n(x)$$

where the c_n are constants?

(3) What can be said about the zeros of $\varphi_n(x)$?

Let us begin by briefly examining self-adjoint differential systems of the second order. Let

$$\mathbf{L} = p_0(x)\frac{d^2}{dx^2} + p_1(x)\frac{d}{dx} + p_2(x)\cdot \tag{2}$$

where $p_0(x) \in C^2(I)$, $p_1(x) \in C^1(I)$, $p_2(x) \in C^0(I)$, and $p_0(x) > 0$ on I. As usual, $I = [a,b]$ is a closed finite interval. The adjoint $\mathbf{L}^*$ of $\mathbf{L}$ is

$$\mathbf{L}^* = p_0(x)\frac{d^2}{dx^2} + [2p_0'(x) - p_1(x)]\frac{d}{dx} + [p_0''(x) - p_1'(x) + p_2(x)]\cdot.$$

Hence for $\mathbf{L}$ to be formally self-adjoint we must have

$$p_0'(x) = p_1(x).$$

In this case $\mathbf{L}y$ may be written as

$$\mathbf{L}y = \frac{d}{dx}(p_0y') + p_2y.$$

Actually, if $\mathbf{M} = q_0(x)\frac{d^2}{dx^2} + q_1(x)\frac{d}{dx} + q_2(x)\cdot$ is any second order linear differential operator [with $q_i(x) \in C^{2-i}(I)$, $i = 0, 1, 2$, and $q_0(x) > 0$ on I], we may always write

$$\mathbf{M} = \mu(x)\,\mathbf{N}$$

where μ is a scalar factor and $\mathbf{N}$ is formally self-adjoint. Viz.: let f be the integrating factor

$$f(x) = \exp\left\{\int_{x_0}^{x}[q_1(\xi)/q_0(\xi)]\,d\xi\right\}, \qquad x_0 \in I.$$

Then

$$\mathbf{M} = \frac{q_0(x)}{f(x)}\,\mathbf{N}$$

where

$$\mathbf{N}y = \frac{d}{dx}(fy') + \left(\frac{f}{q_0}q_2\right)y$$

is formally self-adjoint. Thus, without loss of generality we may always assume a second order linear differential operator to be formally self-adjoint.

Let

$$U_1(y) = 0, \qquad U_2(y) = 0$$

be two linearly independent two-point boundary conditions associated with the formally self-adjoint differential operator $\mathbf{L}$. That is,

$$U_i(y) = A_i(y) + B_i(y), \qquad i = 1, 2 \tag{3}$$

where

$$A_i(y) = a_{i1}y(a) + a_{i2}y'(a), \qquad i = 1, 2$$
$$B_i(y) = b_{i1}y(b) + b_{i2}y'(b), \qquad i = 1, 2.$$

Also, if $y_1(x)$ and $y_2(x)$ form a fundamental set of solutions of the equation $\mathbf{L}y = 0$, then the matrix

$$\| U_i(y_j) \|_{1 \leq i,j \leq 2} \tag{4}$$

is non-singular.

We shall now examine conditions under which the boundary conditions are self-adjoint. Let

$$H(x,\xi) = \frac{-1}{p_0(\xi)W(\xi)} \begin{vmatrix} y_1(x) & y_2(x) \\ y_1(\xi) & y_2(\xi) \end{vmatrix}$$

be the one-sided Green's function for $\mathbf{L}$ (where W is the Wronskian of y_1 and y_2). Since $\mathbf{L}$ is self-adjoint ($p_0' = p_1$) we conclude that

$$W(\xi)p_0(\xi) = W(x_0)p_0(x_0)$$

for any $x_0 \in I$. Thus

$$H(x,\xi) = -\frac{1}{p_0(x_0)W(x_0)} [y_1(x)y_2(\xi) - y_2(x)y_1(\xi)].$$

But from (6.4.8) and Theorem 4 of Chapter 3 we infer

$$C = k \begin{Vmatrix} 0 & 1 \\ -1 & 0 \end{Vmatrix}$$

where k is a non-zero constant. From (3)

$$U_i(y) = A_i(y) + B_i(y), \qquad i = 1, 2$$

and we define $V_i(y)$ as

$$V_i(y) = A_i(y) - B_i(y), \qquad i = 1, 2.$$

Then the condition for self-adjointness (cf. Theorem 8 of Chapter 6) is that the matrix

$$\begin{Vmatrix} V_1(y_1) & V_1(y_2) \\ V_2(y_1) & V_2(y_2) \end{Vmatrix} \cdot \begin{Vmatrix} 0 & 1 \\ -1 & 0 \end{Vmatrix} \cdot \begin{Vmatrix} U_1(y_1) & U_2(y_1) \\ U_1(y_2) & U_2(y_2) \end{Vmatrix} \tag{5}$$

be symmetric. Applying this criterion we see that (5) is equivalent to

$$U_1(y_1)V_2(y_2) + U_2(y_2)V_1(y_1) = U_1(y_2)V_2(y_1) + U_2(y_1)V_1(y_2) \tag{6}$$

which in turn is the same as

$$\det \| A_i(y_j) \|_{1 \leqq i,j \leqq 2} = \det \| B_i(y_j) \|_{1 \leqq i,j \leqq 2}. \tag{7}$$

Consider now the special two-point boundary conditions

$$\begin{aligned} U_1(y) &= \alpha\, y(a) + \beta\, y'(a) \\ U_2(y) &= \gamma\, y(b) + \delta\, y'(b). \end{aligned} \tag{8}$$

In order for U_1 and U_2 to be linearly independent, not both α and β and not both γ and δ may be zero. For the boundary conditions of (8) we see that (7) is automatically satisfied, and hence (8) always represents self-adjoint boundary conditions.

We shall restrict our study of Sturm-Liouville theory to self-adjoint differential systems of the form:

$$\mathbf{L}_\lambda y \equiv \frac{d}{dx}[p(x)y'] + [q(x) + \lambda r(x)]y = 0 \tag{9a}$$

$$\begin{aligned} U_1(y) &\equiv \alpha\, y(a) + \beta\, y'(a) = 0 \\ U_2(y) &\equiv \gamma\, y(b) + \delta\, y'(b) = 0 \end{aligned} \tag{9b}$$

where

(1) The functions $p(x)$, $q(x)$, $r(x)$ are continuous on the closed finite interval $I = [a,b]$, $p(x)$ is of class $C^1(I)$, and $p(x) > 0$, $r(x) > 0$ on I.
(2) Not both α and β and not both γ and δ are zero.
(3) λ is an unrestricted real parameter.

Note that the subscript λ on $\mathbf{L}$ now has a different significance from what it had heretofore.

2. Comparison and Oscillation Theorems

Sturm's fundamental theorem (Theorem 1) concerns the separation of the zeros of solutions of second order self-adjoint differential equations.

Theorem 1. Let

$$\begin{aligned} \mathbf{L}y &= \frac{d}{dx}[p(x)y'] + q(x)y = 0 \\ \mathbf{M}z &= \frac{d}{dx}[p(x)z'] + Q(x)z = 0 \end{aligned} \tag{1}$$

be self-adjoint second order differential equations where $p(x) \in C^1(I)$, $q(x)$, $Q(x) \in C^0(I)$ and $p(x) > 0$ on I where $I = [a,b]$ is a closed finite interval. Let $Q(x) > q(x)$ on the open interval (a,b). Let $\varphi(x)$ be a non-identically zero solution of $\mathbf{L}y=0$. Suppose c and d with $a<c<d<b$ are two consecutive zeros of $\varphi(x)$. Let $\psi(x)$ be any solution of $\mathbf{M}z=0$. Then $\psi(x)$ must vanish at some point of the open interval (c,d).

Proof. From the identity

$$0 = \psi\, \mathbf{L}\varphi - \varphi\, \mathbf{M}\psi = \psi(p\varphi')' - \varphi(p\psi')' + (q-Q)\varphi\psi$$

we infer

$$\psi(p\varphi')' - \varphi(p\psi')' = (Q-q)\varphi\psi$$

and

$$\int_c^d \frac{d}{dx}\{p(x)[\psi(x)\varphi'(x) - \varphi(x)\psi'(x)]\}\, dx = \int_c^d [Q(x) - q(x)]\varphi(x)\psi(x)\, dx. \tag{2}$$

Now suppose $\psi(x)$ does not vanish on (c,d). With no loss of generality we may assume $\psi(x) > 0$ and also $\varphi(x) > 0$ on (c,d). Since $Q(x) > q(x)$, equation (2) implies

$$p(d)[\psi(d)\varphi'(d)-\varphi(d)\psi'(d)]-p(c)[\psi(c)\varphi'(c)-\varphi(c)\psi'(c)]>0. \tag{3}$$

By hypothesis $\varphi(c) = 0 = \varphi(d)$. Thus (3) reduces to

$$p(d)\psi(d)\varphi'(d) - p(c)\psi(c)\varphi'(c) > 0. \tag{4}$$

Now since $\varphi(c)=0$, we must have $\varphi'(c) \neq 0$. Furthermore, since

$\varphi(x) > 0$ on (c,d), $\varphi'(c) > 0$. Similarly, $\varphi'(d) < 0$. Also $p(d) > 0$, $p(c) > 0$, $\psi(d) \geqq 0$, $\psi(c) \geqq 0$. These relations imply that

$$p(d)\psi(d)\varphi'(d) - p(c)\psi(c)\varphi'(c)$$

is non-positive—which contradicts (4).

Corollary. Let $q(x) \equiv Q(x)$ on I and let $\varphi(x)$ and $\psi(x)$ be two linearly independent solutions of $\mathbf{L}y=0$. Then $\psi(x)$ must vanish between two consecutive zeros of $\varphi(x)$.

Proof. As before, let $\varphi(c) = 0 = \varphi(d)$ where $a < c < d < b$. Then (2) implies

$$p(d)\psi(d)\varphi'(d) - p(c)\psi(c)\varphi'(c) = 0. \tag{5}$$

As in the proof of Theorem 1, $\varphi'(c) > 0$, $\varphi'(d) < 0$ and $p(c) > 0$, $p(d) > 0$. If we assume $\psi(x)$ does not vanish on (c,d), then without loss of generality we may assume $\psi(c) \geqq 0$, $\psi(d) \geqq 0$. But $\psi(c) \neq 0 \neq \psi(d)$ since φ and ψ are linearly independent. Thus $\psi(c) > 0$, $\psi(d) > 0$. This implies that $p(d)\psi(d)\varphi'(d) - p(c)\psi(c)\varphi'(c)$ is negative—which contradicts (5).

Further progress in the study of the zeros of the solutions is most effectively achieved by making certain transformations. Consider the differential equation of (1.9a):

$$\frac{d}{dx}(py') + (q + \lambda r)y = 0.$$

Let

$$\begin{aligned} y' &= \frac{z}{p} \\ z' &= -(q+\lambda r)y. \end{aligned} \tag{6}$$

Let x_0 be any point in I. Then if (y_0,z_0) is any pair of real numbers, there exist continuously differentiable functions $y(x)$ and $z(x)$ which satisfy (6) and have the property that

$$\begin{aligned} y(x_0) &= y_0 \\ z(x_0) &= z_0. \end{aligned}$$

If $y(x)$ is a non-trivial solution, then $y(x)$ and $z(x)$ are never zero for the same value of x. For if they were, this would imply y and y'

vanishing for the same value of x. Let

$$\begin{aligned} y(x) &= \rho(x)\sin\theta(x) \\ z(x) &= \rho(x)\cos\theta(x). \end{aligned} \tag{7}$$

Then

$$\rho^2(x) = y^2(x) + z^2(x).$$

Since $\rho(x) \neq 0$ for $x \in I$, and $y(x)$ and $z(x)$ are continuously differentiable, we infer that $\rho(x)$ is single-valued and continuously differentiable on $[a,b]$. Furthermore, since

$$\sin\theta(x) = \frac{y(x)}{\rho(x)}$$

this implies $\theta(x)$ is also single-valued and continuously differentiable on I.

From (7) we see that $y(x)$ can vanish only when $\sin\theta(x)$ does (since $\rho \neq 0$), and $\sin\theta(x)$ vanishes only when $\theta(x)$ is an integral multiple of π. Since we wish to investigate further the zeros of $y(x)$, it will be advantageous to study in some detail the first order equation on $\theta(x)$.

From (6) and (7)

$$\begin{aligned} z = \rho\cos\theta &= py' = p(\rho\sin\theta)' \\ &= p(\rho'\sin\theta + \rho\theta'\cos\theta) \end{aligned} \tag{8}$$

and

$$z' = -(q+\lambda r)y = (\rho\cos\theta)' = \rho'\cos\theta - \rho\theta'\sin\theta. \tag{9}$$

Solving (8) and (9) simultaneously for ρ' and θ' we obtain

$$\rho' = \rho\sin\theta\cos\theta\left(\frac{1}{p} - q - \lambda r\right) \tag{10}$$

and

$$\theta' = \frac{\cos^2\theta}{p} + (q + \lambda r)\sin^2\theta. \tag{11}$$

We now prove our second comparison theorem:

Theorem 2. Let

$$\mathbf{L}y = \frac{d}{dx}(py') + qy = 0$$

$$\mathbf{M}z = \frac{d}{dx}(Pz') + Qz = 0$$

where p, P, q, Q are continuous functions of x on the closed finite interval $I = [a,b]$ and $p, P \in C^1(I)$. Let $\theta(x)$ be related to $\mathbf{L}$ by the transformation (7) and $\Theta(x)$ similarly related to M. Let

$$Q(x) \geqq q(x)$$

$$0 < P(x) \leqq p(x)$$

on $[a,b]$ and

$$\Theta(a) \geqq \theta(a).$$

Then

$$\Theta(x) \geqq \theta(x)$$

on I.

Proof. From (11)

$$(\Theta - \theta)' = \frac{\cos^2 \Theta}{P} - \frac{\cos^2 \theta}{p} + Q \sin^2 \Theta - q \sin^2 \theta.$$

Now add and subtract $\dfrac{\sin^2 \theta}{p} + \left(\dfrac{1}{p} - q\right) \sin^2 \Theta$ to the right-hand side of the above equation to obtain

$$\begin{aligned}
(\Theta - \theta)' &= \left(\frac{1}{p} - q\right) \sin^2 \theta - \left(\frac{1}{p} - q\right) \sin^2 \Theta \\
&\quad + \frac{1}{P}\cos^2 \Theta + \left(\frac{1}{p} - q\right) \sin^2 \Theta - \frac{1}{p}\sin^2 \theta + Q \sin^2 \Theta - \frac{\cos^2 \theta}{p} \\
&= \left(\frac{1}{p} - q\right)(\sin^2 \theta - \sin^2 \Theta) \\
&\quad + \frac{1}{P}\cos^2 \Theta + \frac{1}{p}(1 - \cos^2 \Theta) - (q - Q) \sin^2 \Theta - \frac{1}{p} \\
&= \left[\left(q - \frac{1}{p}\right)(\sin^2 \Theta - \sin^2 \theta)\right] \\
&\quad + \left[\left(\frac{1}{P} - \frac{1}{p}\right) \cos^2 \Theta + (Q - q) \sin^2 \Theta\right].
\end{aligned} \tag{12}$$

The second term in brackets on the right of (12) is non-negative. Let

$$g(x) = \left(\frac{1}{P} - \frac{1}{p}\right) \cos^2 \Theta(x) + [Q(x) - q(x)] \sin^2 \Theta(x)$$

be the function of x obtained by replacing Θ and θ by their solutions of (11). Then (12) may be written (with $\eta = \Theta - \theta$) as

$$\eta' = h(x)\eta + g(x) \tag{13}$$

where

$$h(x) = \left[q(x) - \frac{1}{p(x)}\right]\left[\frac{\sin^2 \Theta(x) - \sin^2 \theta(x)}{\Theta(x) - \theta(x)}\right]$$

is a continuous function of x on I, and $g(x) \geqq 0$. Thus (13) implies

$$\eta' \geqq h(x)\eta$$

or, since $\eta(a) \geqq 0$,

$$\eta(x) \geqq 0. \tag{14}$$

But $\eta = \Theta - \theta$. Thus (14) implies

$$\Theta(x) \geqq \theta(x).$$

Corollary. If $Q(x) > q(x)$ on (a,b) then $\Theta(x) > \theta(x)$ on $(a,b]$.

Proof. Suppose for some $c > a$,

$$\Theta(x) = \theta(x)$$

for $x \in [a,c]$. Then (12) can hold with $Q(x) > q(x)$ only if $P(x) \equiv p(x)$ and $\Theta(x)$ is an integral multiple of π. But then

$$\Theta' = \frac{\cos^2 \Theta}{P} + Q \sin^2 \Theta$$

would imply

$$\frac{1}{P(x)} = 0$$

on $[a,c]$, which is a contradiction.

By Theorem 2, $\Theta(x) \geqq \theta(x)$ on $[a,b]$. We have just shown that there exists no $c > a$ such that $\Theta(x) = \theta(x)$ on $[a,c]$. Thus there must exist a sequence of points $\{x_n' | n=0, 1, 2, \cdots\}$ converging to a such that $\Theta(x_n) > \theta(x_n)$. Hence $\eta(x_k) > 0$ and $\eta(x) > 0$ for $x > x_k$ [cf. (14)]. For k sufficiently large, this implies $\Theta(x) > \theta(x)$ on $(a,b]$.

The boundary conditions associated with (1.9a) are given by (1.9b). Thus, in terms of the transformation (6), the first boundary condition $U_1(y) = 0$ becomes

$$\alpha\, y(a) + \beta \frac{z(a)}{p(a)} = 0. \tag{15}$$

Since α and β are not both zero we may write (15) as

$$\frac{\alpha}{\sqrt{\alpha^2 + \dfrac{\beta^2}{p^2(a)}}}\, y(a) + \frac{\beta/p(a)}{\sqrt{\alpha^2 + \dfrac{\beta^2}{p^2(a)}}}\, z(a) = 0.$$

Thus there exists a unique θ_a with $0 \leqq \theta_a < \pi$ such that

$$y(a) \cos \theta_a - z(a) \sin \theta_a = 0. \tag{16}$$

Similarly, a consideration of the second boundary condition $U_2(y) = 0$ of (1.9b) leads to

$$y(b) \cos \theta_b - z(b) \sin \theta_b = 0, \qquad 0 < \theta_b \leqq \pi. \tag{17}$$

We now wish to investigate the dependence of the solutions $\theta(x,\lambda)$ of (11) on the parameter λ.

Lemma. Let

$$\theta'(x) = \frac{\cos^2 \theta(x)}{p(x)} + [q(x) + \lambda r(x)] \sin^2 \theta(x) \tag{18}$$

and satisfy the boundary condition

$$\theta(a,\lambda) = \theta_a, \qquad 0 \leqq \theta_a < \pi$$

where $p(x)$, $q(x)$, $r(x)$ are continuous on $[a,b]$ and $p(x) > 0$, $r(x) > 0$ on $[a,b]$. Let λ be an unrestricted real parameter. Then

$$\lim_{\lambda \to -\infty} \theta(b,\lambda) = 0$$

$$\lim_{\lambda \to +\infty} \theta(b,\lambda) = \infty.$$

Proof. By Theorem 2, as λ increases, $\theta(x,\lambda)$ is an increasing function of λ for fixed x. Furthermore, since $\theta_a \geqq 0$ and $\theta'(x) > 0$ when $\theta(x,\lambda) = 0$ we must have $\theta(x,\lambda) \geqq 0$. (For if $\theta < 0$ this would imply $\theta' \leqq 0$ at $\theta = 0$.)

Choose constants A and B such that

$$0 < B < \pi$$

$$\theta_a < A < \pi.$$

Then (cf. Fig. 1) if the solution θ is to cross AB we must have

$$\theta' \geqq \frac{B - A}{b - a}$$

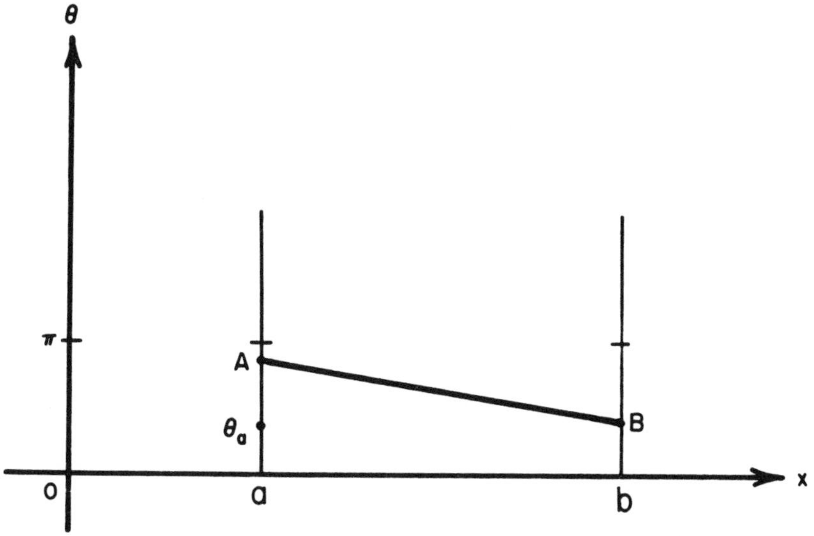

Fig. 1

at the crossing point (x,θ) on AB. Now choose a Λ such that for all $\lambda < \Lambda$,

$$\frac{\cos^2\theta}{p(x)} + [q(x) + \lambda r(x)]\sin^2\theta < \frac{B - A}{b - a}$$

for all (x,θ) on AB. This is possible since θ is bounded away from 0 and π, and $r(x) > 0$ on $[a,b]$. Hence

$$0 \leqq \theta(b,\lambda) \leqq B$$

for $\lambda < \Lambda$. Since $B > 0$ may be made arbitrarily small,

$$\lim_{\lambda\to-\infty} \theta(b,\lambda) = 0.$$

To prove the second result of the lemma, choose a $C > 0$ such that

$$\frac{C - \theta_a}{b - a} \geqq \min \frac{1}{p(x)}$$

on $[a,b]$. Let the line $\theta_a C$ intersect the horizontal line $\theta = k\pi$ at the point P_k. Through P_k draw a line of slope s_k, $k = 1, 2, \cdots$, where

$$0 < s_k \leqq \min \frac{1}{2p(x)}, \qquad a \leqq x \leqq b, \qquad k = 1, 2, \cdots,$$

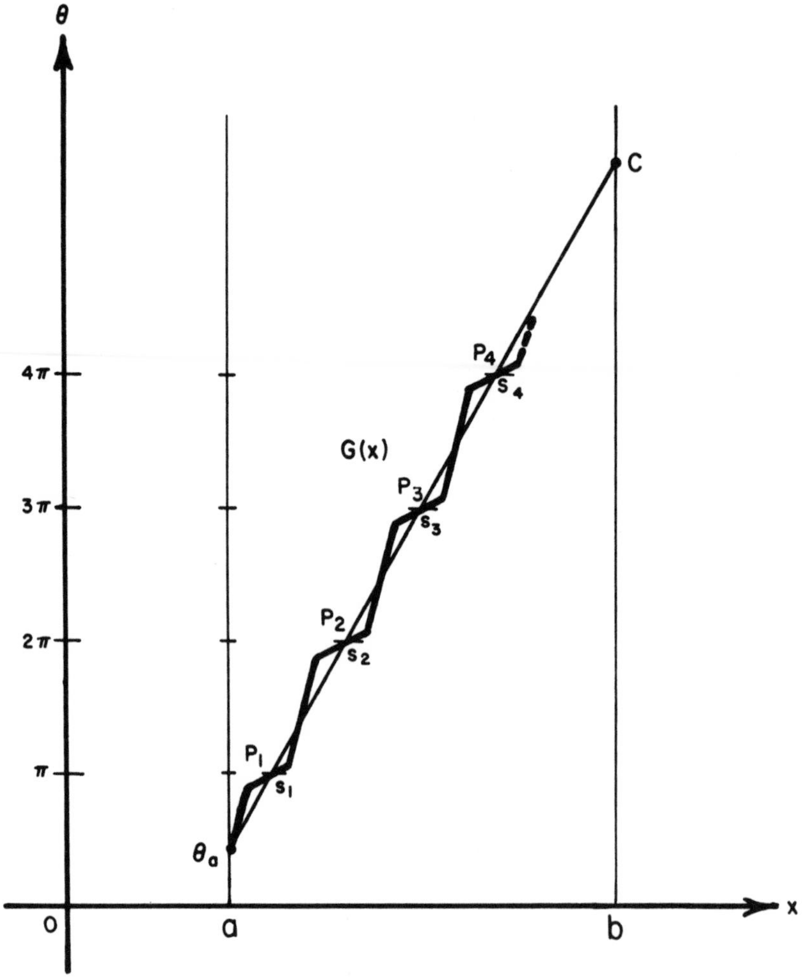

Fig. 2

in a neighborhood of P_k. Then draw a polygonal path as in Fig. 2. Call this path $G(x)$. Then $G(x)$ has a right- and left-hand derivative at every point of $[a,b]$. Let us define $G'(x)$ as the right-hand derivative.

We shall now show that it is possible to choose a Λ such that

$$\theta'(x,\lambda) > G'(x)$$

for all x in $[a,b]$ and $\lambda > \Lambda$. Assume for the moment this is true. Then since $\theta(a,\lambda) = \theta_a \geqq 0$, this implies $\theta(x,\lambda) > G(x)$ on $(a,b]$ and in particular $\theta(b,\lambda) \geqq C$ for $\lambda > \Lambda$. Since C may be made arbitrarily large

$$\lim_{\lambda \to \infty} \theta(b,\lambda) = \infty.$$

Toward this end, suppose first that x lies on one of the lines of slope s_k. Choose a Λ' such that for all $\lambda > \Lambda'$

$$q(x) + \lambda r(x) > \frac{1}{p(x)}$$

for all x in $[a,b]$. Then

$$\theta' = \frac{\cos^2\theta}{p} + (q+\lambda r)\sin^2\theta \geqq \frac{\cos^2\theta}{p} + \frac{\sin^2\theta}{p} = \frac{1}{p}$$

and

$$\theta'(x) \geqq \frac{1}{p(x)} > \frac{1}{2p(x)} \geqq \min \frac{1}{2p(x)} \geqq s_k, \qquad k = 1, 2, \cdots.$$

If x does not lie in one of the neighborhoods of π, it is bounded away from multiples of π, and $\sin^2\theta \geqq K > 0$ for some constant K. Thus we can choose a Λ'' such that

$$\frac{\cos^2\theta}{p(x)} + [q(x) + \lambda r(x)]\sin^2\theta > G'(x)$$

for all $\lambda > \Lambda''$ and all x not in a neighborhood of P_k. If we let $\Lambda = \max(\Lambda', \Lambda'')$ we see that

$$\theta'(x,\lambda) > G'(x)$$

for all $\lambda > \Lambda$.

We are now in a position to make a quantitative statement regarding the zeros of the solutions of (1.9).

Let $\theta(x,\lambda)$ be a solution of (11) which assumes the initial value

$$\theta(a,\lambda) = \theta_a, \qquad 0 \leqq \theta_a < \pi.$$

We leave it to the reader to show that $\theta(x,\lambda)$ is continuous† in λ. Since $\lim_{\lambda\to-\infty} \theta(b,\lambda) = 0$ and $\theta_b > 0$ and $\lim_{\lambda\to\infty} \theta(b,\lambda) = \infty$, we can

†See Murray and Miller, *Existence theorems for ordinary differential equations*, page 72.

choose a λ_0 such that

$$\theta(b,\lambda_0) = \theta_b.$$

Then $\theta(x,\lambda_0)$ is a solution of (11) with the properties:

$$\theta(a,\lambda_0) = \theta_a$$
$$\theta(b,\lambda_0) = \theta_b.$$

Let $\varphi_0(x)$ be a solution of $\mathbf{L}_{\lambda_0}y = 0$ corresponding to $\theta(x,\lambda_0)$. Then

$$\alpha\varphi_0(a) + \beta\varphi_0'(a)$$

$$= \alpha\,\rho(a)\sin\theta\,(a,\lambda_0) + \beta\,\rho(a)\frac{\cos\theta\,(a,\lambda_0)}{p(a)}$$

$$= \rho(a)\left[\alpha\sin\theta_a + \beta\frac{\cos\theta_a}{p(a)}\right]$$

$$= \rho(a)\sqrt{\alpha^2 + \frac{\beta^2}{p^2(a)}}\left\{\frac{\alpha}{\sqrt{\alpha^2 + \dfrac{\beta^2}{p^2(a)}}}\sin\theta_a + \frac{\beta/p(a)}{\sqrt{\alpha^2 + \dfrac{\beta^2}{p^2(a)}}}\cos\theta_a\right\}$$

$$= \rho(a)\sqrt{\alpha^2 + \frac{\beta^2}{p^2(a)}}\{\cos\theta_a\sin\theta_a - \sin\theta_a\cos\theta_a\} = 0.$$

Similarly

$$\gamma\,\varphi_0(b) + \delta\,\varphi_0'(b) = 0.$$

Thus $\varphi_0(x)$ is a non-identically zero solution of $\mathbf{L}_{\lambda_0}y = 0$ which satisfies the two homogeneous boundary conditions $U_1(y) = 0 = U_2(y)$.

Now we assert that $\varphi_0(x)$ is never zero on (a,b). For suppose $x' \in (a,b)$ were such that $\varphi_0(x') = 0$. Then from (7), $\sin\theta(x') = 0$ and $\theta(x') = k\pi$ where k is an integer; and from (11), $\theta'(x') > 0$. Now $\theta(a,\lambda_0) < \pi$ and $\theta(b,\lambda_0) \leqq \pi$. Thus if $\theta(x') = k\pi$ $(k > 0)$ at an interior point, there must exist another interior point x'' such that $\theta(x'') = k\pi$ and $\theta'(x'') < 0$. This is a contradiction.

Now let $\lambda_1 > \lambda_0$ be the unique value of λ such that $\theta(x,\lambda_1)$ is a solution of (11) with the property that

$$\theta(a,\lambda_1) = \theta_a$$
$$\theta(b,\lambda_1) = \theta_b + \pi.$$

Let $\varphi_1(x)$ be the corresponding solution of $\mathbf{L}_{\lambda_1}y = 0$. Then, as above, we show that

$$U_1(\varphi_1(x)) = 0$$
$$U_2(\varphi_1(x)) = 0.$$

Thus $\varphi_1(x)$ is a non-identically zero solution of $\mathbf{L}_{\lambda_1}y = 0$ which satisfies the two boundary conditions $U_1(y) = 0 = U_2(y)$. Then there is an x' in the open interval (a,b) such that $\theta(x',\lambda_1) = \pi$. Thus $\varphi_1(x)$ has a zero in (a,b) (at x'). As above, we conclude that $\theta(x,\lambda_1)$ assumes the value π just once in (a,b). Thus $\varphi_1(x)$ has exactly one zero in (a,b).

In general, there exists an infinite number of values $\{\lambda_n | n = 0, 1, 2, \cdots\}$ such that

$$\lambda_0 < \lambda_1 < \cdots < \lambda_n < \cdots$$

and $\theta(b,\lambda_n) = \theta_b + n\pi$. Since $\theta(x,\lambda_n)$ assumes the value $k\pi$, $1 \leqq k \leqq n$, exactly once, $\varphi_n(x)$ has precisely n zeros in (a,b).

Let M be any number, no matter how large, and let $\theta(b,M) = K$. Choose an m so large that $\theta_b + m\pi > K$. Then there is a $\lambda_m > M$ such that $\theta(b,\lambda_m) = \theta_b + m\pi$. Thus

$$\lim_{n\to\infty} \lambda_n = \infty.$$

We have therefore proved the following theorem:

Theorem 3. Let

$$\mathbf{L}_\lambda y \equiv \frac{d}{dx}[p(x)y'] + [q(x) + \lambda r(x)]y = 0$$

where $p(x)$, $q(x)$, $r(x)$ are continuous on some closed finite interval $I = [a,b]$, $p(x) \in C^1(I)$, and $p(x)$ and $r(x)$ are positive on I. Let

$$U_1(y) \equiv \alpha\, y(a) + \beta\, y'(a) = 0$$
$$U_2(y) \equiv \gamma\, y(b) + \delta\, y'(b) = 0$$

be two two-point boundary conditions such that $\alpha^2 + \beta^2 \neq 0 \neq \gamma^2 + \delta^2$. Then there exists a sequence of real numbers $\{\lambda_n | n = 0, 1, 2, \cdots\}$ such that

$$\lambda_0 < \lambda_1 < \cdots < \lambda_n < \cdots$$

and $\lim_{n\to\infty} \lambda_n = \infty$. For each λ_n there is a unique non-identically zero function $\varphi_n(x)$ such that

$$\begin{aligned} \mathbf{L}_{\lambda_n}\varphi_n &\equiv 0 \\ U_1(\varphi_n) &\equiv 0 \\ U_2(\varphi_n) &\equiv 0 \end{aligned}$$

and $\varphi_n(x)$ has precisely n zeros on (a,b).

3. Properties of the Characteristic Functions

In this section we shall consider certain properties of the characteristic functions that will be used in establishing the closure and completeness theorems of the next sections.

Let $I = [a,b]$ be a closed finite interval. Let $p(x) \in C^1(I)$, $q(x)$, $r(x) \in C^0(I)$ and $p(x) > 0$, $r(x) > 0$ on I. Then we shall call the differential system

$$\begin{aligned} \mathbf{L}_\lambda y &\equiv \frac{d}{dx}[p(x)y'] + [q(x) + \lambda r(x)]y = 0 \\ U_1(y) &\equiv \alpha\, y(a) + \beta\, y'(a) = 0 \qquad (1) \\ U_2(y) &\equiv \gamma\, y(b) + \delta\, y'(b) = 0 \end{aligned}$$

(where $\alpha^2 + \beta^2 \neq 0 \neq \gamma^2 + \delta^2$) a *Sturm-Liouville system.* We have seen in Theorem 3 that there exist real numbers $\{\lambda_n | n = 0, 1, 2, \cdots\}$ and corresponding functions $\{\varphi_n(x) | n = 0, 1, 2, \cdots\}$ which satisfy (1). That is,

$$\begin{aligned} \mathbf{L}_{\lambda_i}\varphi_i(x) &\equiv 0 \\ U_1(\varphi_i) &\equiv 0 \qquad i = 0, 1, 2, \cdots \\ U_2(\varphi_i) &\equiv 0. \end{aligned}$$

The λ_n are called *characteristic numbers* and the $\varphi_n(x)$ are called *characteristic functions.* Furthermore,

$$\lambda_0 < \lambda_1 < \cdots < \lambda_n < \cdots$$

and $\lim_{n\to\infty} \lambda_n = \infty$. The $\varphi_n(x)$, $n = 0, 1, 2, \cdots$ are non-identically zero functions of class $C^2(I)$ and $\varphi_n(x)$ has n zeros on the open interval (a,b), $n = 0, 1, 2, \cdots$.

Our first important result will be to establish the orthogonality of the characteristic functions. We recall that a set of functions

$\{h_n(x)\}$ is said to be *orthogonal* on the interval $[c,d]$ with respect to the non-negative, non-identically zero weighting function $w(x)$ if

$$\int_c^d w(x)\, h_i(x)\, h_j(x)\, dx = 0, \qquad i \neq j$$

$$\neq 0, \qquad i = j.$$

We shall now show that the characteristic functions of the Sturm-Liouville system (1) are orthogonal on $[a,b]$ with respect to $r(x)$.

Theorem 4. The characteristic functions of a Sturm-Liouville system are orthogonal.

Proof. Let $\{\varphi_j(x) \mid j = 0, 1, 2, \cdots\}$ be the characteristic functions of (1) and $\{\lambda_j \mid j = 0, 1, 2, \cdots\}$ the corresponding characteristic numbers. Then

$$\mathbf{L}_{\lambda_j}\varphi_j(x) = \frac{d}{dx}[p(x)\varphi_j'(x)] + [q(x) + \lambda_j r(x)]\varphi_j(x) = 0$$

and

$$\mathbf{L}_{\lambda_k}\varphi_k(x) = \frac{d}{dx}[p(x)\varphi_k'(x)] + [q(x) + \lambda_k r(x)]\varphi_k(x) = 0.$$

Thus

$$\begin{aligned} 0 &= \varphi_k\, \mathbf{L}_{\lambda_j}\varphi_j - \varphi_j\, \mathbf{L}_{\lambda_k}\varphi_k \\ &= \varphi_k \frac{d}{dx}(p\varphi_j') - \varphi_j \frac{d}{dx}(p\varphi_k') + (\lambda_j - \lambda_k) r\varphi_j\varphi_k \qquad (2) \\ &= \frac{d}{dx}[p(\varphi_k\varphi_j' - \varphi_j\varphi_k')] - (\lambda_k - \lambda_j) r\varphi_j\varphi_k. \end{aligned}$$

Let

$$\Delta(x) = \varphi_k(x)\varphi_j'(x) - \varphi_j(x)\varphi_k'(x). \qquad (3)$$

Then (2) implies

$$(\lambda_k - \lambda_j)\int_a^b r(x)\varphi_j(x)\varphi_k(x)\, dx = p(b)\Delta(b) - p(a)\Delta(a).$$

Now the characteristic functions satisfy the boundary conditions. In particular

$$U_1(\varphi_k) \equiv \alpha\, \varphi_k(a) + \beta\, \varphi_k(a) = 0$$

$$U_1(\varphi_j) \equiv \alpha\, \varphi_j(a) + \beta\, \varphi_j'(a) = 0.$$

Since not both α and β are zero, we must have $\Delta(a) = 0$. Similarly $\Delta(b) = 0$. If $k \neq j$, $\lambda_k - \lambda_j \neq 0$, and

$$\int_a^b r(x)\varphi_j(x)\varphi_k(x)\,dx = 0, \qquad j \neq k.$$

Since $r(x) > 0$ and $\varphi_j(x) \not\equiv 0$ we have

$$\int_a^b r(x)\varphi_j(x)\varphi_k(x)\,dx > 0, \qquad j = k.$$

If

$$\int_a^b r(x)\,\varphi_j^2(x)\,dx = A_j^2 > 0$$

we shall normalize the characteristic functions by considering

$$\pm\frac{1}{A_j}\,\varphi_j(x), \qquad j = 0, 1, 2, \cdots.$$

We shall assume hereafter that the characteristic functions have been so normalized. In this case

$$\int_a^b r(x)\varphi_j(x)\varphi_k(x)\,dx = \delta_{jk}, \qquad j, k = 0, 1, 2, \cdots. \tag{4}$$

When (4) holds, we call the $\{\varphi_n(x) | n = 0, 1, 2, \cdots\}$ *orthonormal.*

Next we shall prove a sequence of lemmas culminating in Theorem 5. This theorem is crucial in establishing the closure of the characteristic functions (cf. the next section).

Lemma 1. Let $\{\varphi_n(x) | n=0, 1, 2, \cdots\}$ be the set of characteristic functions of the Sturm-Liouville problem (1). Let

$$\psi_j(x) = p(x)[\varphi_0(x)\varphi_{j+1}'(x) - \varphi_{j+1}(x)\varphi_0'(x)], \qquad j=0, 1, 2, \cdots.$$

Then there exist functions $P(x)$, $Q(x)$, $R(x)$ which are continuous and non-zero on (a,b) such that

$$\frac{d}{dx}[P(x)\psi_j'] + [Q(x) + \Lambda_j R(x)]\psi_j = 0, \qquad j = 0, 1, 2, \cdots.$$

Furthermore, $P(x)\psi_j'(x)$ has a continuous derivative on (a,b) for

$j = 0, 1, 2, \cdots$ and the $\{\Lambda_j | j = 0, 1, 2, \cdots\}$ form a strictly increasing sequence of real numbers without limit.

Proof. Let

$$\Delta_j(x) = \varphi_0(x)\varphi_j'(x) - \varphi_j(x)\varphi_0'(x), \qquad j = 1, 2, \cdots$$

and

$$\psi_j(x) = p(x)\Delta_{j+1}(x), \qquad j = 0, 1, 2, \cdots.$$

Then

$$\frac{d}{dx}\psi_j = \varphi_0 \frac{d}{dx}(p\varphi_{j+1}') - \varphi_{j+1}\frac{d}{dx}(p\varphi_0').$$

But

$$\frac{d}{dx}(p\varphi_0') = -(q+\lambda_0 r)\varphi_0$$

$$\frac{d}{dx}(p\varphi_{j+1}') = -(q + \lambda_{j+1}r)\varphi_{j+1}.$$

Thus

$$\frac{d}{dx}\psi_j = (\lambda_0 - \lambda_{j+1})r\varphi_0\varphi_{j+1}. \tag{5}$$

Let

$$P(x) = \frac{1}{r(x)\varphi_0^2(x)}.$$

Then

$$\begin{aligned}\frac{d}{dx}(P\psi_j') &= (\lambda_0 - \lambda_{j+1})\frac{d}{dx}\left(\frac{\varphi_{j+1}}{\varphi_0}\right) = (\lambda_0 - \lambda_{j+1})\frac{\Delta_{j+1}}{\varphi_0^2} \\ &= \frac{\lambda_0\psi_j}{p\,\varphi_0^2} - \frac{\lambda_{j+1}\psi_j}{p\,\varphi_0^2}.\end{aligned} \tag{6}$$

Let

$$Q(x) = -\frac{\lambda_0}{p(x)\varphi_0^2(x)}$$

$$R(x) = \frac{1}{p(x)\varphi_0^2(x)}$$

$$\Lambda_j = \lambda_{j+1}.$$

Then (6) reduces to

$$\frac{d}{dx}(P\psi_j') + (Q + \Lambda_j R)\psi_j = 0.$$

The other conclusions of the lemma are immediately evident.

Lemma 2. Let $\{\varphi_n(x) | n = 0, 1, 2, \cdots\}$ be the set of characteristic functions of the Sturm-Liouville system (1). Let

$$\psi_j(x) = p(x)[\varphi_0(x)\varphi'_{j+1}(x) - \varphi_{j+1}(x)\varphi'_0(x)], \qquad j = 0, 1, 2, \cdots$$

as in Lemma 1. Then

(i) $\lim_{x\to a} \psi_j(x) = 0 = \lim_{x\to b} \psi_j(x), \qquad j = 0, 1, 2, \cdots$

(ii) $\lim_{x\to a} \dfrac{\varphi_j(x)}{\varphi_0(x)} \neq 0 \neq \lim_{x\to b} \dfrac{\varphi_j(x)}{\varphi_0(x)}, \qquad j = 0, 1, 2, \cdots$

(iii) $\lim_{x\to a} P(x)[\psi_0(x)\psi'_j(x) - \psi_j(x)\psi'_0(x)] = 0$

$\lim_{x\to b} P(x)[\psi_0(x)\psi'_j(x) - \psi_j(x)\psi'_0(x)] = 0 \qquad j = 0, 1, 2, \cdots$

(iv) $\lim_{x\to a} \dfrac{\psi_j(x)}{\psi_0(x)} \neq 0 \neq \lim_{x\to b} \dfrac{\psi_j(x)}{\psi_0(x)}, \qquad j = 0, 1, 2, \cdots$

where $P(x) = 1/r(x)\varphi_0^2(x)$, $a < x < b$.

Proof. We prove (ii) first. Let

$$\Delta_j(x) = \varphi_0(x)\varphi'_j(x) - \varphi_j(x)\varphi'_0(x), \qquad j = 1, 2, \cdots.$$

We have seen in Theorem 4 and elsewhere that

$$\Delta_j(a) = 0.$$

Thus if $\varphi_0(a) \neq 0$ we must have $\varphi_j(a) \neq 0$. For suppose $\varphi_j(a) = 0$. Then $\varphi'_j(a)$ must be unequal to zero. This would imply $\Delta_j(a) = \varphi_0(a)\varphi'_j(a) \neq 0$ which is a contradiction. On the other hand, if $\varphi_0(a) = 0$, then $\varphi_j(a) = 0$. For suppose $\varphi_j(a) \neq 0$. Then since $\varphi_0(a) = 0$ implies $\varphi'_0(a) \neq 0$, we must have $\Delta_j(a) = -\varphi_j(a)\varphi'_0(a) \neq 0$, which is a contradiction. By l'Hospital's rule,

$$\lim_{x\to a} \frac{\varphi_j(x)}{\varphi_0(x)} = \frac{\varphi'_j(a)}{\varphi'_0(a)} \neq 0.$$

A similar argument establishes

$$\lim_{x\to b} \frac{\varphi_j(x)}{\varphi_0(x)} \neq 0.$$

To prove (i) we note that

$$\psi_j(x) = p(x)\Delta_{j+1}(x)$$

and $\Delta_{j+1}(a) = 0 = \Delta_{j+1}(b)$ while $p(x) > 0$ on $[a,b]$.

To prove (iii), we write from (5) that

$$P(x)[\psi_0(x)\psi_j'(x) - \psi_j(x)\psi_0'(x)]$$
$$= P(x)[(\lambda_0-\lambda_{j+1})r(x)\varphi_0(x)\varphi_{j+1}(x)\psi_0(x) - (\lambda_0-\lambda_1)r(x)\varphi_0(x)\varphi_1(x)\psi_j(x)]$$
$$= (\lambda_0-\lambda_{j+1})\psi_0(x)\frac{\varphi_{j+1}(x)}{\varphi_0(x)} - (\lambda_0-\lambda_1)\psi_j(x)\frac{\varphi_1(x)}{\varphi_0(x)}.$$

Now $\psi_j(a) = 0, j = 0, 1, 2, \cdots$ and by (ii), $\lim_{x\to a} \varphi_j(x)/\varphi_0(x)$ exists, $j = 0, 1, 2, \cdots$. Thus

$$\lim_{x\to a} P(x)[\psi_0(x)\psi_j'(x) - \psi_j(x)\psi_0'(x)] = 0.$$

A similar argument establishes the result at $x = b$.

Finally, to prove (iv) we note that

$$\lim_{x\to a}\frac{\psi_j(x)}{\psi_0(x)} = \lim_{x\to a}\frac{\psi_j'(x)}{\psi_0'(x)}$$

by l'Hospital's rule since $\psi_j(a) = 0 = \psi_0(a)$. But by (5)

$$\frac{\psi_j'(x)}{\psi_0'(x)} = \frac{(\lambda_0-\lambda_{j+1})}{(\lambda_0-\lambda_1)}\frac{\varphi_0(x)}{\varphi_1(x)}\frac{\varphi_{j+1}(x)}{\varphi_0(x)}.$$

An application of (ii) establishes (iv) at $x = a$. Similarly we prove

$$\lim_{x\to b}\frac{\psi_j(x)}{\psi_0(x)} \neq 0.$$

Lemma 3. Let $\{\psi_j(x) | j = 0, 1, 2, \cdots\}$ be as in Lemmas 1 and 2. Then $\psi_j(x)$ has at most j zeros in (a,b), $j = 0, 1, 2, \cdots$.

Proof. By (5)

$$\psi_j'(x) = (\lambda_0-\lambda_{j+1})\, r(x)\, \varphi_0(x)\, \varphi_{j+1}(x)$$

and $\varphi_{j+1}(x)$ has $j+1$ zeros on (a,b), while $r(x)$ and $\varphi_0(x)$ do not vanish on the open interval (a,b). Thus $\psi_j(x)$ cannot have more than j zeros on (a,b). [Recall that $\psi_j(a) = 0 = \psi_j(b)$].

Definition. Let $\{\chi_j(x) | j = 0, 1, 2, \cdots\}$ be a set of function continuous on the open interval (a,b). We shall call $\{\chi_j(x)\}$ a *set of Sturm-Liouville functions* if $\{\chi_j(x)\}$ has the following properties:

(1) There exists a function $\pi(x)$ positive and continuous on (a,b) such that $\pi(x)\chi_j'(x)$ has a continuous derivative on (a,b).

(2) There exists a sequence of real numbers $\{\ell_j | j = 0, 1, 2, \cdots\}$ such that

$$\ell_0 < \ell_1 < \cdots < \ell_n < \cdots$$

and $\lim_{n\to\infty} \ell_n = \infty$; and functions $v(x)$ and $\rho(x)$ continuous on (a,b) with $\rho(x) > 0$ on (a,b) such that

$$\frac{d}{dx}[\pi(x)\chi_j'(x)] + [v(x) + \ell_j\rho(x)]\chi_j(x) = 0.$$

(3) $$\lim_{x\to a} \pi(x)[\chi_j'(x)\chi_0(x) - \chi_0'(x)\chi_j(x)] = 0$$
$$= \lim_{x\to b} \pi(x)[\chi_j'(x)\chi_0(x) - \chi_0'(x)\chi_j(x)].$$

(4) $$\lim_{x\to a} \frac{\chi_j(x)}{\chi_0(x)} \neq 0 \neq \lim_{x\to b} \frac{\chi_j(x)}{\chi_0(x)}.$$

(5) $\chi_j(x)$ has at most j zeros on (a,b).

Note that every set of characteristic functions is a set of Sturm-Liouville functions.

Now as an easy consequence of Lemmas 1, 2, 3 we have:

Lemma 4. Let $\{\varphi_j(x) | j = 0, 1, 2, \cdots\}$ be a set of Sturm-Liouville functions satisfying the equation

$$(p\varphi_j')' + (q + \lambda_j r)\varphi_j = 0.$$

Then the derived set of functions $\{\psi_j(x) | j = 0, 1, 2, \cdots\}$ where

$$\psi_j(x) = p(x)[\varphi_0(x)\varphi_{j+1}'(x) - \varphi_{j+1}(x)\varphi_0'(x)], \qquad j = 0, 1, 2, \cdots$$

is also a set of Sturm-Liouville functions.

The main consequence of the above lemma is Theorem 5 below, which will be invoked at a crucial point in the proof of closure (Lemma 3 of Section 4).

Theorem 5. Let $\{\varphi_j(x) | j = 0, 1, 2, \cdots\}$ be a set of Sturm-Liouville functions. Let m be a positive integer. Let k_j, $1 \leqq j \leqq m$, be constants such that

$$k_1\varphi_0(x) + k_2\varphi_1(x) + \cdots + k_m\varphi_{m-1}(x)$$

has at least m zeros on the open interval (a,b). Then

$$k_j = 0, \qquad 1 \leqq j \leqq m.$$

Proof. Suppose there exist sets of Sturm-Liouville functions $\{\varphi_j(x)\}$, integers m, and constants k_j, $1 \leqq j \leqq m$, not all zero such that

$$\sum_{j=1}^{m} k_j \, \varphi_{j-1}(x)$$

has at least m zeros on (a,b). Then there must exist an integer M such that if $0 < \mu \leqq M$, there exists no set of Sturm-Liouville functions with the property that constants k_j not all zero exist such that

$$\sum_{j=1}^{\mu} k_j \, \varphi_{j-1}(x)$$

has at least μ zeros on (a,b). For example, let $\mu = 1$.

Let

$$f(x) = \sum_{j=1}^{M} k_j \, \varphi_{j-1}(x), \qquad a < x < b,$$

where M is minimal, have at least M zeros on (a,b). Since M is minimal, we must have $k_M \neq 0$. Consider

$$\frac{f(x)}{\varphi_0(x)} = \sum_{j=1}^{M} k_j \frac{\varphi_{j-1}(x)}{\varphi_0(x)}, \qquad a < x < b.$$

Then differentiating, we have

$$\frac{d}{dx}\frac{f(x)}{\varphi_0(x)} = \sum_{j=2}^{M} k_j \frac{\Delta_{j-1}(x)}{\varphi_0^2(x)}, \qquad a < x < b$$

where

$$\Delta_{j-1}(x) = \varphi_0(x)\varphi'_{j-1}(x) - \varphi_{j-1}(x)\varphi'_0(x), \qquad 2 \leqq j \leqq M.$$

Let

$$\psi_{j-1}(x) = p(x)\Delta_j(x), \qquad 1 \leqq j \leqq M-1,$$

where $p(x)$ comes from the equation

$$(p\varphi'_j)' + (q+\lambda_j r)\varphi_j = 0.$$

Then

$$p\,\varphi_0^2 \frac{d}{dx}\left(\frac{f}{\varphi_0}\right) = k_2\psi_0(x) + k_3\psi_1(x) + \cdots + k_M\psi_{M-2}(x)$$

has at least $M - 1$ zeros on (a,b). By Lemma 4, $\{\psi_j(x) | j = 0, 1, 2, \cdots\}$ is a set of Sturm-Liouville functions. But M was minimal. Thus $k_2 = k_3 = \cdots = k_M = 0$ and

$$\frac{f}{\varphi_0} = k_1$$

or

$$f(x) = k_1 \varphi_0(x).$$

But $\varphi_0(x) \neq 0$ on the open interval (a,b). Thus $k_1 = 0$.

4. Closure

Let $\{\varphi_n(x) | n = 0, 1, 2, \cdots\}$ be a set of characteristic functions of a Sturm-Liouville system. The main purpose of this section is to show that $\{\varphi_n(x)\}$ is *closed*. That is, if $\psi(x)$ is any function continuous on $[a,b]$ which is orthogonal to all members of $\{\varphi_n\}$, then $\psi(x) \equiv 0$. This crucial result, Theorem 6, will be preceded by a sequence of four lemmas—the most important being Lemmas 1 and 4.

We shall consider the Sturm-Liouville system described by (3.1), where the characteristic functions $\{\varphi_n(x) | n = 0, 1, 2, \cdots\}$ will be assumed to be orthonormal.

Lemma 1. If there exists a function $\psi(x)$ which is continuous and not identically zero on $I = [a,b]$ with the property that

$$\int_a^b r(x)\psi(x)\varphi_i(x)\, dx = 0, \qquad i = 0, 1, 2, \cdots,$$

where the $\{\varphi_n(x)\}$ are the characteristic functions, then there exists a function $\chi(x) \in C^2(I)$ and not identically zero which satisfies the boundary conditions $U_1(\chi) = 0 = U_2(\chi)$ and has the property that

$$\int_a^b r(x)\chi(x)\varphi_i(x)\, dx = 0, \qquad i = 0, 1, 2, \cdots.$$

Proof. Consider the non-homogeneous equation

$$\mathbf{L}_\lambda y = r(x)\psi(x) \tag{1}$$

(where λ is not a characteristic number), together with the homogeneous boundary conditions

$$\begin{aligned} U_1(y) &= 0 \\ U_2(y) &= 0. \end{aligned} \tag{2}$$

Since λ is not a characteristic number, the completely homogeneous system

$$\begin{aligned} \mathbf{L}_\lambda y &= 0 \\ U_1(y) &= 0 \\ U_2(y) &= 0 \end{aligned}$$

is incompatible. Thus there exists a unique function $\chi(x)$ (which can be expressed in terms of the Green's function of $\mathbf{L}_\lambda$) that satisfies (1) and (2). Furthermore, $\chi(x) \not\equiv 0$ since $\mathbf{L}_\lambda \chi(x) = r(x)\psi(x)$ and $\psi(x) \not\equiv 0$. By Green's formula

$$\begin{aligned} &\int_a^b [\varphi_i(x)\, \mathbf{L}_\lambda \chi(x) - \chi(x)\, \mathbf{L}_\lambda^* \varphi_i(x)]\, dx \\ &\quad = U_1(\chi)V_4(\varphi_i) + U_2(\chi)V_3(\varphi_i) + U_3(\chi)V_2(\varphi_i) + U_4(\chi)V_1(\varphi_i). \end{aligned} \tag{3}$$

Since the differential system is self-adjoint, V_1 and V_2 are linear combinations of U_1 and U_2. But $U_1(\chi) = 0 = U_2(\chi)$. Thus (3) implies

$$\int_a^b \varphi_i(x)\, \mathbf{L}_\lambda \chi(x)\, dx = \int_a^b \chi(x)\, \mathbf{L}_\lambda^* \varphi_i(x)\, dx. \tag{4}$$

Now $\mathbf{L}_\lambda = \mathbf{L}_\lambda^*$ since $\mathbf{L}_\lambda$ is formally self-adjoint. Also

$$\mathbf{L}_\lambda \chi = r(x)\psi(x).$$

Thus (4) implies

$$\int_a^b r(x)\psi(x)\varphi_i(x)\, dx = \int_a^b \chi(x)\, \mathbf{L}_\lambda \varphi_i(x)\, dx. \tag{5}$$

But by hypothesis, the left-hand side of (5) is zero for $i = 0, 1, 2, \cdots$. Thus

$$\int_a^b \chi(x)\, \mathbf{L}_\lambda \varphi_i(x)\, dx = 0, \qquad i = 0, 1, 2, \cdots. \tag{6}$$

Now

$$\mathbf{L}_\lambda \varphi_i(x) = \frac{d}{dx}[p(x)\varphi_i'(x)] + [q(x) + \lambda r(x)]\varphi_i(x)$$

and

$$\mathbf{L}_{\lambda_i} \varphi_i(x) = \frac{d}{dx}[p(x)\varphi_i'(x)] + [q(x) + \lambda_i r(x)]\varphi_i(x) = 0$$

where λ_i is the characteristic number corresponding to $\varphi_i(x)$. Thus

$$\mathbf{L}_\lambda \varphi_i(x) = (\lambda - \lambda_i) r(x)\varphi_i(x)$$

and (6) becomes

$$(\lambda - \lambda_i)\int_a^b \chi(x) r(x)\varphi_i(x)\,dx = 0, \qquad i = 0, 1, 2, \cdots. \tag{7}$$

Since λ_i is a characteristic number and λ is not, $\lambda - \lambda_i \neq 0$ and our lemma is established.

Lemma 2. Let $\chi(x) \in C^2(I)$ satisfy the boundary conditions $U_1(\chi) = 0$, $U_2(\chi) = 0$. If $\chi(x)$ vanishes at all points of the open interval (a,b) which are zeros of $\varphi_n(x)$, then

$$\int_a^b \chi(x)\,\mathbf{L}_0\chi(x)\,dx + \lambda_n \int_a^b r(x)\,\chi^2(x)\,dx \leqq 0.$$

Proof. Let

$$\Delta(x) = \varphi_n(x)\chi'(x) - \chi(x)\varphi_n'(x)$$

be the Wronskian of $\varphi_n(x)$ and $\chi(x)$, and let

$$F(x) = \frac{p(x)\chi(x)}{\varphi_n(x)}\,\Delta(x) \tag{8}$$

at all points x in $[a,b]$ which are not zeros of $\varphi_n(x)$. If $z \in (a,b)$ is a zero of $\varphi_n(x)$, then by l'Hospital's rule

$$\lim_{x \to z} \frac{\chi(x)}{\varphi_n(x)} = \frac{\chi'(z)}{\varphi_n'(z)}.$$

Since φ_n and φ_n' cannot vanish for the same value of x, we must have $\varphi_n'(z) \neq 0$. We shall therefore define $F(x)$ at $x = z$ as

$$F(z) = \lim_{x \to z} F(x).$$

Note that $F(z) = 0$ and that $F(x)$ is now continuous in the open interval (a,b).

Consider $x = a$. Since φ_n and χ satisfy the first boundary condition,

$$U_1(\varphi_n) = \alpha\, \varphi_n(a) + \beta\, \varphi_n'(a) = 0$$

$$U_1(\chi) = \alpha\, \chi(a) + \beta\, \chi'(a) = 0.$$

We recall that not both α and β are zero. Thus the determinant of the coefficients, namely $\Delta(a)$, must vanish. Explicitly,

$$\varphi_n(a)\, \chi'(a) - \chi(a)\, \varphi_n'(a) = 0.$$

Now if $\varphi_n(a) = 0$ we must have $\chi(a) = 0$ since $\varphi_n'(a) \neq 0$. Then if we define $F(a)$ as

$$F(a) = \lim_{\substack{x \to a \\ x > a}} F(x)$$

and similarly define $F(b)$ if $\varphi_n(b) = 0$, the function $F(x)$ becomes continuous on the closed interval $[a,b]$. We also note that

$$F(a) = 0 = F(b) \tag{9}$$

since $\Delta(a) = 0 = \Delta(b)$ regardless of whether $\varphi_n(x)$ vanishes at a and/or b.

One can also verify that dF/dx exists and is continuous on $[a,b]$. Now

$$\frac{dF}{dx} = p\,\frac{\Delta^2}{\varphi_n^2} + \frac{\chi}{\varphi_n}\,(p\Delta)'. \tag{10}$$

From

$$\mathbf{L}_0\chi = \frac{d}{dx}(p\chi') + (q\chi)$$

and

$$\mathbf{L}_0\varphi_n = \frac{d}{dx}(p\varphi_n') + (q\varphi_n) \tag{11}$$

we obtain

$$\varphi_n\, \mathbf{L}_0\chi - \chi\, \mathbf{L}_0\varphi_n = \varphi_n \frac{d}{dx}(p\chi') - \chi \frac{d}{dx}(p\varphi_n')$$

$$= \frac{d}{dx}(p\Delta). \tag{12}$$

This enables us to write (10) as

$$\frac{dF}{dx} = p\,\frac{\Delta^2}{\varphi_n^2} + \frac{\chi}{\varphi_n}\,(\varphi_n\,\mathbf{L}_0\chi - \chi\,\mathbf{L}_0\varphi_n). \tag{13}$$

Furthermore,

$$\mathbf{L}_{\lambda_n}\varphi_n = \frac{d}{dx}(p\varphi_n') + (q+\lambda_n r)\varphi_n = 0$$

and together with (11) we conclude

$$\mathbf{L}_0\varphi_n = -\lambda_n r\varphi_n. \tag{14}$$

We may therefore rewrite (13) as

$$\frac{dF}{dx} = p\,\frac{\Delta^2}{\varphi_n^2} + \chi\,\mathbf{L}_0\chi + \chi^2\lambda_n r.$$

Now by (9),

$$0 = F(b) - F(a) = \int_a^b \frac{dF}{dx}\,dx$$

$$= \int_a^b p(x)\frac{\Delta^2(x)}{\varphi_n^2(x)}\,dx + \int_a^b [\chi(x)\,\mathbf{L}_0\chi(x) + \lambda_n r(x)\chi^2(x)]\,dx.$$

Since $\int_a^b p(\Delta/\varphi_n)^2\,dx$ is non-negative we infer

$$0 \geqq \int_a^b [\chi(x)\,\mathbf{L}_0\chi(x) + \lambda_n r(x)\chi^2(x)]\,dx$$

—which is our lemma.

Lemma 3. Let $\chi(x) \in C^2(I)$ satisfy the boundary conditions $U_1(\chi) = 0$, $U_2(\chi) = 0$. Let $x_1, x_2, \cdots, x_n$ be the distinct interior points of (a,b) at which $\varphi_n(x)$ vanishes. Then there exist constants c_j, $0 \leqq j \leqq n-1$, such that

$$\chi(x_i) = \sum_{j=0}^{n-1} c_j\,\varphi_j(x_i), \qquad 1 \leqq i \leqq n.$$

Proof. The existence of the c_j, $0 \leqq j \leqq n-1$, will be guaranteed if the matrix $\Phi = \|\varphi_j(x_i)\|_{1 \leqq i \leqq n,\, 0 \leqq j \leqq n-1}$ is non-singular. Suppose then that Φ is singular. Then there would exist constants k_j, $0 \leqq j \leqq n-1$, not all zero such that

$$\sum_{j=0}^{n-1} k_j\, \varphi_j(x_i) = 0, \qquad 1 \leqq i \leqq n.$$

Thus the function

$$\sum_{j=0}^{n-1} k_j\, \varphi_j(x)$$

would have at least n zeros (namely, x_i, $1 \leqq i \leqq n$) in (a,b). By Theorem 5, $k_j = 0$, $0 \leqq j \leqq n-1$. The contradiction proves the theorem.

Lemma 4. Let $\chi(x) \in C^2(I)$ satisfy the boundary conditions $U_1(\chi) = 0$, $U_2(\chi) = 0$ and be orthogonal to $\varphi_j(x)$, $0 \leqq j \leqq n-1$; that is,

$$\int_a^b r(x)\chi(x)\varphi_j(x)\, dx = 0, \qquad 0 \leqq j \leqq n-1.$$

Then

$$\int_a^b \chi(x)\, \mathbf{L}_0\chi(x)\, dx + \lambda_n \int_a^b r(x)\, \chi^2(x)\, dx \leqq 0.$$

Proof. By Lemma 3 there exist constants c_j, $0 \leqq j \leqq n-1$, such that

$$\chi(x_i) = \sum_{j=0}^{n-1} c_j\, \varphi_j(x_i), \qquad 1 \leqq i \leqq n.$$

Define $g(x)$ by the equation

$$g(x) = \chi(x) - \sum_{j=0}^{n-1} c_j\, \varphi_j(x). \tag{15}$$

Then $g(x)$ vanishes at the zeros of $\varphi_n(x)$. Since $\chi(x)$ and $\varphi_k(x)$, $k = 0, 1, 2, \cdots$ satisfy the boundary conditions, so does $g(x)$. That is,

$$U_1(g) = 0, \qquad U_2(g) = 0.$$

By Lemma 2,

$$\int_a^b g(x)\, \mathbf{L}_0 g(x)\, dx + \lambda_n \int_a^b r(x)\, g^2(x)\, dx \leqq 0. \tag{16}$$

Now $g(x)$ is given by (15). Hence the first term of (16) becomes

$$\int_a^b g(x)\,\mathbf{L}_0 g(x)\,dx = \int_a^b \left[\chi(x) - \sum_{j=0}^{n-1} c_j\varphi_j(x)\right] \mathbf{L}_0 \left[\chi(x) - \sum_{j=0}^{n-1} c_j\varphi_j(x)\right] dx. \tag{17}$$

As in (14),

$$\mathbf{L}_0\varphi_j = -\lambda_j r\varphi_j, \qquad j = 0, 1, 2, \cdots, \tag{18}$$

and since the φ_j are normalized characteristic functions,

$$\int_a^b r(x)\varphi_j(x)\varphi_k(x)\,dx = \delta_{jk}.$$

Thus (17) becomes

$$\begin{aligned}\int_a^b g(x)\,\mathbf{L}_0 g(x)\,dx = \int_a^b \chi(x)\,\mathbf{L}_0\chi(x)\,dx - \sum_{j=0}^{n-1} c_j \int_a^b \varphi_j(x)\,\mathbf{L}_0\chi(x)\,dx \\ + \sum_{k=0}^{n-1} \lambda_k c_k \int_a^b r(x)\chi(x)\varphi_k(x)\,dx - \sum_{k=0}^{n-1} \lambda_k c_k^2.\end{aligned} \tag{19}$$

But $\chi(x)$ is orthogonal to $\varphi_0(x), \varphi_1(x), \cdots \varphi_{n-1}(x)$. And, [cf. (4)],

$$\int_a^b \varphi_j(x)\,\mathbf{L}_0\chi(x)\,dx = \int_a^b \chi(x)\,\mathbf{L}_0\varphi_j(x)\,dx$$

provided $\mathbf{L}_0$ is self-adjoint and $U_i(\varphi_j) = 0 = U_i(\chi)$, $i = 1, 2$. Equation (17) then simplifies to

$$\int_a^b g(x)\,\mathbf{L}_0 g(x)\,dx = \int_a^b \chi(x)\,\mathbf{L}_0\chi(x)\,dx - \sum_{j=0}^{n-1} c_j \int_a^b \chi(x)\,\mathbf{L}_0\varphi_j(x)\,dx - \sum_{k=0}^{n-1} \lambda_k c_k^2.$$

From (18)

$$\int_a^b \chi(x)\,\mathbf{L}_0\varphi_j(x)\,dx = -\lambda_j \int_a^b r(x)\chi(x)\varphi_j(x)\,dx$$

which equals zero by hypothesis for $0 \leqq j \leqq n - 1$. Hence we finally obtain

$$\int_a^b g(x)\,\mathbf{L}_0 g(x)\,dx = \int_a^b \chi(x)\,\mathbf{L}_0\chi(x)\,dx - \sum_{k=0}^{n-1} \lambda_k c_k^2. \tag{20}$$

Returning to (16) we may write

$$\int_a^b r(x)\, g^2(x)\, dx = \int_a^b r(x)\Big[\chi(x) - \sum_{j=0}^{n-1} c_j\varphi_j(x)\Big]^2 dx$$
$$= \int_a^b r(x)\, \chi^2(x)\, dx + \sum_{j=0}^{n-1} c_j^2. \qquad (21)$$

Substituting (20) and (21) in (16) gives:

$$\int_a^b \chi(x)\, \mathbf{L}_0\chi(x)\, dx + \lambda_n \int_a^b r(x)\,\chi^2(x)\, dx + \sum_{j=0}^{n-1}(\lambda_n - \lambda_j)c_j^2 \leqq 0.$$

Since $\lambda_n - \lambda_j > 0$ for $0 \leqq j \leqq n - 1$, our lemma is proved.

We are now in a position to prove our main result.

Theorem 6. Let $\{\varphi_n(x) | n = 0, 1, 2, \cdots\}$ be the normalized characteristic functions of the Sturm-Liouville system (3.1). Let $\psi(x)$ be a function continuous on I with the property that

$$\int_a^b r(x)\psi(x)\varphi_i(x)\, dx = 0, \qquad i = 0, 1, 2, \cdots.$$

(That is, ψ is orthogonal to $\{\varphi_n\}$.) Then

$$\psi(x) \equiv 0$$

on $[a.b]$.

Proof. Suppose $\psi(x) \not\equiv 0$ on $[a,b]$. Then by Lemma 1 there exists a non-identically zero function $\chi(x)$ orthogonal to the $\varphi_j(x)$, $j = 0, 1, 2, \cdots$ which satisfies the boundary conditions $U_1(\chi) = 0$, $U_2(\chi) = 0$. But $\chi(x)$ must be identically zero; otherwise the inequality of Lemma 4 could not hold for all n since $\lim_{n\to\infty} \lambda_n = \infty$. The contradiction proves the theorem.

5. Completeness

Let $\{\varphi_n(x) | n = 0, 1, 2, \cdots\}$ be the normalized characteristic functions of the Sturm-Liouville system (3.1). We have seen in Theorem

4 that the $\{\varphi_n(x)\}$ are orthonormal. That is:

$$\int_a^b r(x)\varphi_i(x)\varphi_j(x)\,dx = \delta_{ij}, \qquad i, j = 0, 1, 2, \cdots. \tag{1}$$

We have also seen (Theorem 6) that the $\{\varphi_n(x)\}$ are *closed.* That is:

$$\int_a^b r(x)\psi(x)\varphi_i(x)\,dx = 0, \qquad i = 0, 1, 2, \cdots$$

for a function $\psi(x)$ continuous on $[a,b]$, implies $\psi(x) \equiv 0$.

Suppose now that $f(x)$ is an arbitrary integrable function defined on $[a,b]$. We ask whether there exist constants f_n, $n = 0, 1, 2, \cdots$ such that

$$f(x) = \sum_{n=0}^{\infty} f_n\varphi_n(x). \tag{2}$$

Formally, if we multiply both sides of (2) by $r(x)\varphi_k(x)$ and integrate from a to b:

$$\int_a^b r(x)f(x)\varphi_k(x)\,dx = \sum_{n=0}^{\infty} f_n \int_a^b r(x)\varphi_n(x)\varphi_k(x)\,dx = \sum_{n=0}^{\infty} f_n\delta_{nk} = f_k.$$

Thus

$$f_k = \int_a^b r(x)f(x)\varphi_k(x)\,dx, \qquad k = 0, 1, 2, \cdots. \tag{3}$$

The above formal manipulations would have led to (2) even if we had started with a proper subset of the $\{\varphi_n\}$. Thus the truth of (2) is certainly not obvious. We wish to investigate various conditions under which the expansion in characteristic functions converges.

We note first that even if $f(x)$ is only integrable on $[a,b]$, the f_k of (3) always exist. We shall call

$$\sum_{k=0}^{\infty} f_k\,\varphi_k(x) \tag{4}$$

where the f_k are determined by (3) the *Fourier series* associated with $f(x)$ and write

$$f(x) \sim \sum_{k=0}^{\infty} f_k\,\varphi_k(x). \tag{5}$$

Thus we may always write (5) for an integrable function $f(x)$. Let $F_n(x)$ be the nth partial sum of (4). Then we wish to know under what conditions $F_n(x)$ converges to $f(x)$ as n tends to infinity. In this connection we shall prove two theorems. The first (Theorem 7) will give sufficient conditions on a function $f(x)$ in order that

$$\lim_{n\to\infty} F_n(x) = f(x), \qquad x \in [a,b].$$

In other words, we have point-wise convergence. In Theorem 10 we shall show that if $f(x)$ is merely integrable, then

$$\underset{n\to\infty}{\text{l.i.m.}}\ F_n(x) = f(x). \tag{6}$$

That is, $F_n(x)$ converges in mean square to $f(x)$:

$$\lim_{n\to\infty} \int_a^b r(x)[F_n(x) - f(x)]^2\,dx = 0. \tag{7}$$

We now turn to the proofs of these important theorems. Let $\{\varphi_n(x)|n = 0, 1, 2, \cdots\}$ be the characteristic functions of the Sturm-Liouville system (3.1). Let $g(x)$ be continuous and piece-wise differentiable on $[a,b]$. Let $g(a) = 0$ if $\varphi_0(a) = 0$ and let $g(b) = 0$ if $\varphi_0(b) = 0$. We shall call such a function a *Sturm function.* Then we have:

Theorem 7. Let $\{\varphi_n(x)|n = 0, 1, 2, \cdots\}$ be the normalized characteristic functions of the Sturm-Liouville system (3.1). Let $f(x)$ be a Sturm function. Let

$$F_n(x) = \sum_{k=0}^{n} f_k\, \varphi_k(x)$$

where f_k is given by (3). Then $F_n(x)$ converges uniformly on $[a,b]$ to $f(x)$.

Suppose, for the moment, that $F_n(x)$ converges uniformly on $[a,b]$ to $g(x)$. Then $g(x)$ is continuous on $[a,b]$ and

$$g(x) = \sum_{k=0}^{\infty} f_k\, \varphi_k(x). \tag{8}$$

Furthermore, if we multiply the above equation by any function continuous on $[a,b]$, then we may integrate term by term. Multiply both sides of (8) by $r(x)\varphi_j(x)$ and integrate:

$$\int_a^b r(x)g(x)\varphi_j(x)\,dx = \sum_{k=0}^{\infty} f_k \int_a^b r(x)\varphi_k(x)\varphi_j(x)\,dx = f_j. \tag{9}$$

Thus, from (3) and (9)

$$\int_a^b r(x)[g(x) - f(x)]\varphi_j(x)\,dx = 0, \qquad j = 0, 1, 2, \cdots.$$

Since $g(x) - f(x)$ is continuous and orthogonal to $\varphi_n(x)$ for $n = 0, 1, 2, \cdots$ we infer by Theorem 6 that

$$g(x) - f(x) \equiv 0.$$

Hence

$$g(x) = f(x), \qquad x \in [a,b].$$

It follows, therefore, that if we can merely prove that $F_n(x)$ converges uniformly we shall have established Theorem 7. Toward this end we first prove a lemma.

Lemma. Let $\{\omega_n(x) | n = 1, 2, \cdots\}$ be defined and integrable on $[a,b]$. Let

$$\int_a^b \omega_i(x)\omega_j(x)\,dx = \delta_{ij}, \qquad i, j = 1, 2, \cdots.$$

Let $K(x,\xi)$ be defined on the square $\{a \leqq x \leqq b, a \leqq \xi \leqq b\}$ and be integrable with respect to x for each ξ in $[a,b]$. Let

$$\int_a^b K^2(x,\xi)\,dx < M$$

for some finite constant M and all ξ in $[a,b]$. Let $F(x)$ be integrable on $[a,b]$. Then the series

$$\sum_{n=1}^{\infty} \left[\int_a^b F(\zeta)\,\omega_n(\zeta) d\zeta\right] \int_a^b K(x,\xi)\,\omega_n(x)\,dx$$

converges uniformly for ξ in $[a,b]$.

Proof. From

$$0 \leqq \int_a^b \left[K(x,\xi) - \sum_{k=1}^{n} \omega_k(x) \int_a^b K(t,\xi)\, \omega_k(t)\, dt \right]^2 dx$$

$$= \int_a^b K^2(x,\xi)\, dx - \sum_{k=1}^{n} \left[\int_a^b K(t,\xi)\omega_k(t)\, dt \right]^2$$

we conclude that

$$\sum_{k=1}^{\infty} \left[\int_a^b K(t,\xi)\, \omega_k(t)\, dt \right]^2 < M.$$

Similarly

$$\sum_{n=1}^{\infty} \left[\int_a^b F(\zeta)\, \omega_n(\zeta)\, d\zeta \right]^2 \leqq \int_a^b F^2(x)\, dx.$$

Now let $\epsilon > 0$ be assigned. Choose an N so large that

$$\sum_{n=m}^{m+p} \left[\int_a^b F(\zeta)\, \omega_n(\zeta)\, d\zeta \right]^2 < \frac{\epsilon}{M}$$

for all $m > N$ and $p > 0$. By the Cauchy-Schwarz inequality

$$\left[\sum_{n=m}^{m+p} \int_a^b F(\zeta)\, \omega_n(\zeta)\, d\zeta \int_a^b K(t,\xi)\omega_n(t)\, dt \right]^2$$

$$\leqq \sum_{n=m}^{m+p} \left[\int_a^b F(\zeta)\omega_n(\zeta)\, d\zeta \right]^2 \sum_{n=m}^{m+p} \left[\int_a^b K(t,\xi)\omega_n(t)\, dt \right]^2$$

$$\leqq M \sum_{n=m}^{m+p} \left[\int_a^b F(\zeta)\omega_n(\zeta)\, d\zeta \right]^2 < \epsilon.$$

Thus by the Cauchy convergence theorem

$$\sum_{n=1}^{\infty} \int_a^b F(\zeta)\omega_n(\zeta)\, d\zeta \int_a^b K(t,\xi)\omega_n(t)\, dt$$

converges uniformly for all ξ in $[a,b]$.

We shall now identify the Sturm-Liouville problem with the above lemma. Let $\{\varphi_n(x) | n = 0, 1, 2, \cdots\}$ be the normalized characteristic functions of the Sturm-Liouville system (3.1). Let $\{\lambda_n | n = 0, 1, 2, \cdots\}$ be the corresponding characteristic numbers. Define

$$\Delta_i(x) = \varphi_0(x)\varphi_i'(x) - \varphi_i(x)\varphi_0'(x), \qquad i = 1, 2, \cdots$$

and let

$$\begin{aligned} \omega_n(x) &= \frac{\sqrt{p(x)}}{\sqrt{\lambda_n - \lambda_0}} \frac{\Delta_n(x)}{\varphi_0(x)} \qquad n = 1, 2, \cdots \\ &= \frac{\sqrt{p(x)}}{\sqrt{\lambda_n - \lambda_0}} \varphi_0(x) \frac{d}{dx} \frac{\varphi_n(x)}{\varphi_0(x)}. \end{aligned} \tag{10}$$

We shall show first that the above $\omega_n(x)$ satisfy the conditions required of them by the lemma.

The $\omega_n(x)$ are certainly continuous on (a,b). By (ii) of Lemma 2 of Section 3,

$$\lim_{x \to a} \omega_n(x) \qquad \text{and} \qquad \lim_{x \to b} \omega_n(x)$$

both exist. Thus $\omega_n(x)$, $n = 1, 2, \cdots$ are integrable on $[a,b]$. In fact, if we define $\omega_n(a)$ as $\lim_{x \to a} \omega_n(x)$ and $\omega_n(b)$ as $\lim_{x \to b} \omega_n(x)$, then the functions $\omega_n(x)$ become continuous on $[a,b]$.

Now

$$\begin{aligned} \omega_n(x)\omega_m(x) &= \frac{p(x)}{\sqrt{(\lambda_n - \lambda_0)(\lambda_m - \lambda_0)}} \frac{\Delta_n(x)}{\varphi_0(x)} \frac{\Delta_m(x)}{\varphi_0(x)} \\ &= \frac{p(x)}{\sqrt{(\lambda_n - \lambda_0)(\lambda_m - \lambda_0)}} \Delta_n(x) \frac{d}{dx} \frac{\varphi_m(x)}{\varphi_0(x)} \end{aligned}$$

and integrating by parts, we have

$$\begin{aligned} \int_a^b \omega_n(x)\omega_m(x)\, dx &= -\frac{1}{\sqrt{(\lambda_n - \lambda_0)(\lambda_m - \lambda_0)}} \int_a^b \frac{\varphi_m(x)}{\varphi_0(x)} \frac{d}{dx} [p(x)\Delta_n(x)]\, dx \\ &= \sqrt{\frac{\lambda_n - \lambda_0}{\lambda_m - \lambda_0}} \int_a^b \frac{\varphi_m(x)}{\varphi_0(x)} [r(x)\varphi_0(x)\varphi_n(x)]\, dx \end{aligned}$$

[cf. Lemma 2 of Section 3 and (3.5)]. By the orthogonality of the $\varphi_n(x)$,

$$\int_a^b \omega_n(x)\, \omega_m(x)\, dx = \delta_{nm}, \qquad n, m = 1, 2, \cdots. \tag{11}$$

We now construct the $F(x)$ of the lemma. Let $f(x)$ be a Sturm function. Define

$$F(x) = \sqrt{p(x)}\, \frac{[\varphi_0(x) f'(x) - f(x)\varphi_0'(x)]}{\varphi_0(x)} \tag{12}$$

on (a,b) at all points where $f'(x)$ exists. Then $F(x)$ is integrable on $[a,b]$ if $\varphi_0(a) \neq 0 \neq \varphi_0(b)$. If $\varphi_0(a) = 0$, define $F(a)$ as

$$F(a) = \lim_{x \to a} F(x)$$

(which limit exists). Similarly define $F(b)$ if $\varphi_0(b) = 0$.

Now

$$\int_a^b F(x)\omega_n(x)\, dx = \frac{1}{\sqrt{\lambda_n - \lambda_0}} \int_a^b p(x)\Delta_n(x) \frac{d}{dx} \frac{f(x)}{\varphi_0(x)}\, dx$$

$$= \sqrt{\lambda_n - \lambda_0} \int_a^b \frac{f(x)}{\varphi_0(x)}\, r(x)\varphi_n(x)\varphi_0(x)\, dx$$

after an integration by parts. Hence

$$\int_a^b F(x)\omega_n(x)\, dx = \sqrt{\lambda_n - \lambda_0} \int_a^b r(x) f(x) \varphi_n(x)\, dx, \qquad n = 1, 2, \cdots. \tag{13}$$

It remains but to construct the function $K(x,\xi)$ of the lemma. Let

$$\begin{aligned} K(x,\xi) &= \frac{\varphi_0(\xi)}{\varphi_0(x)\sqrt{p(x)}} \int_a^x r(\zeta)\, \varphi_0^2(\zeta)\, d\zeta, \qquad a \leqq x < \xi \\ &= -\frac{\varphi_0(\xi)}{\varphi_0(x)\sqrt{p(x)}} \int_x^b r(\zeta)\varphi_0^2(\zeta)\, d\zeta, \qquad \xi < x \leqq b \qquad (14) \\ &= 0, \qquad x = \xi. \end{aligned}$$

Then $K(x,\xi)$ is defined for all x and ξ in the closed square $\{a \leqq x \leqq b, a \leqq \xi \leqq b\}$ except possibly at $x = a$ and/or $x = b$. If $\varphi_0(a) = 0$, then for $\xi \neq a$ fixed,

$$\lim_{x \to a} K(x,\xi) = 0$$

while $K(x,a) = 0$. We shall in this case therefore define $K(a,\xi)$ as zero. Similarly we define $K(b,\xi)$ as zero if $\varphi_0(b) = 0$.

Now for ξ fixed

$$K(\xi-,\xi) - K(\xi+,\xi) = \frac{1}{\sqrt{p(\xi)}} \int_a^\xi r(\zeta)\varphi_0^2(\zeta)\, d\zeta + \frac{1}{\sqrt{p(\xi)}} \int_\xi^b r(\zeta)\varphi_0^2(\zeta)\, d\zeta$$

$$= \frac{1}{\sqrt{p(\xi)}}$$

and K has a simple discontinuity along the line $x = \xi$.

We now wish to show that $|K(x,\xi)|$ is uniformly bounded. This will then imply the finiteness of $\int_a^b K^2(x,\xi)\, dx$ for all ξ in $[a,b]$. Consider first

$$a \leqq x < \xi \leqq b.$$

Then from (14)

$$K(x,\xi) = \frac{\varphi_0(\xi)}{\varphi_0(x)\sqrt{p(x)}} \int_a^x r(\zeta)\varphi_0^2(\zeta)\, d\zeta$$

which is continuous for $x < b$. If $\varphi_0(b) \neq 0$, there is nothing to prove. Suppose $\varphi_0(b) = 0$. Then by definition

$$\varphi_0'(b) = \lim_{\xi \to b} \frac{\varphi_0(b) - \varphi_0(\xi)}{b - \xi} = -\lim_{\xi \to b} \frac{\varphi_0(\xi)}{b - \xi}$$

and for $|b - \xi| \neq 0$ and sufficiently small,

$$\frac{1}{2} \frac{|\varphi_0(\xi)|}{|b-\xi|} \leqq |\varphi_0'(b)| \leqq 2 \frac{|\varphi_0(\xi)|}{|b-\xi|}.$$

Similarly

$$\frac{1}{2} \frac{|\varphi_0(x)|}{|b-x|} \leqq |\varphi_0'(b)| \leqq 2 \frac{|\varphi_0(x)|}{|b-x|}$$

for $|b - x| \neq 0$ and sufficiently small. Thus

$$\frac{\dfrac{1}{2}\dfrac{|\varphi_0(\xi)|}{|b-\xi|}}{2\dfrac{|\varphi_0(x)|}{|b-x|}} \leqq 1$$

or

$$\frac{|\varphi_0(\xi)|}{|\varphi_0(x)|} \leqq 4\frac{|b-\xi|}{|b-x|}.$$

Hence if $x < \xi < b$ and $|x-b|$ is small,

$$\frac{|\varphi_0(\xi)|}{|\varphi_0(x)|} < 4,$$

that is, it is bounded.

If $\varphi_0(a) = 0$ we treat the case $\xi < x$ when x and ξ are close to a in a similar manner.

Now, cf. (10),

$$\int_a^b K(x,\xi)\omega_n(x)\,dx = \int_a^\xi K(x,\xi)\omega_n(x)\,dx + \int_\xi^b K(x,\xi)\omega_n(x)\,dx$$

$$= \frac{\varphi_0(\xi)}{\sqrt{\lambda_n-\lambda_0}}\left[\int_a^\xi \frac{d}{dx}\frac{\varphi_n(x)}{\varphi_0(x)}\,dx\int_a^x r(\zeta)\varphi_0^2(\zeta)\,d\zeta\right.$$

$$\left.+\int_\xi^b \frac{d}{dx}\frac{\varphi_n(x)}{\varphi_0(x)}\,dx\int_b^x r(\zeta)\varphi_0^2(\zeta)\,d\zeta\right]$$

$$\mp\frac{\varphi_0(\xi)}{\sqrt{\lambda_n-\lambda_0}}\left[\frac{\varphi_n(\xi)}{\varphi_0(\xi)}\int_a^\xi r(\zeta)\varphi_0^2(\zeta)\,d\zeta - \int_a^\xi \varphi_n(x)r(x)\varphi_0(x)\,dx\right.$$

$$\left.-\frac{\varphi_n(\xi)}{\varphi_0(\xi)}\int_b^\xi r(\zeta)\varphi_0^2(\zeta)\,d\zeta - \int_\xi^b \varphi_n(x)r(x)\varphi_0(x)\,dx\right]$$

upon integrating by parts. Thus

$$\int_a^b K(x,\xi)\omega_n(x)\,dx = \frac{\varphi_0(\xi)}{\sqrt{\lambda_n-\lambda_0}}\left[\frac{\varphi_n(\xi)}{\varphi_0(\xi)}\right] = \frac{\varphi_n(\xi)}{\sqrt{\lambda_n-\lambda_0}} \qquad (15)$$

since

$$\int_a^b r(x)\varphi_n(x)\varphi_0(x)\,dx = 0, \qquad n = 1, 2, \cdots,$$

and

$$\int_a^b r(\zeta)\,\varphi_0^2(\zeta)\,d\zeta = 1.$$

With the definitions (10), (12), (14) of $\omega_n(x)$, $F(x)$, $K(x,\xi)$ respectively, we see by virtue of (13) and (15) that

$$\left[\int_a^b F(\zeta)\omega_n(\zeta)\,d\zeta\right]\left[\int_a^b K(x,\xi)\omega_n(x)\,dx\right]$$
$$= \sqrt{\lambda_n - \lambda_0}\int_a^b r(x)f(x)\varphi_n(x)\,dx\,\frac{\varphi_n(\xi)}{\sqrt{\lambda_n - \lambda_0}}.$$

Since the $\{\omega_n(x)|n = 1, 2, \cdots\}$ are orthogonal on $[a,b]$ by (11), the preceding lemma now implies that

$$\sum_{n=1}^{\infty}\left[\int_a^b r(\xi)f(\xi)\varphi_n(\xi)\,d\xi\right]\varphi_n(x)$$

converges uniformly on $[a,b]$. Hence the sequence of partial sums $\{F_n(x)\}$ where

$$F_n(x) = \sum_{k=0}^{n}\left[\int_a^b r(\xi)f(\xi)\varphi_k(\xi)\,d\xi\right]\varphi_k(x)$$

also has this property and Theorem 7 is established.

As an immediate consequence of Theorem 7 we may conclude that:

Theorem 8. Let $\{\varphi_n(x)|n = 0, 1, 2, \cdots\}$ be the normalized characteristic functions of the Sturm-Liouville system (3.1). Let $g(x)$ be a Sturm function. Then given any $\epsilon > 0$ there exists an N such that

$$|g(x) - G_n(x)| < \epsilon$$

for all $n > N$ and all x in $[a,b]$ where

$$G_n(x) = \sum_{k=0}^{n} g_k \varphi_k(x) \tag{16}$$

and

$$g_k = \int_a^b r(x)g(x)\varphi_k(x)\,dx, \qquad k = 0, 1, 2, \cdots.$$

Now let $f(x)$ be integrable on $[a,b]$. We wish to show that the partial sum

$$F_n(x) = \sum_{k=0}^{n} f_k \varphi_k(x)$$

where the f_k are given by (3) converges in the mean to $f(x)$ (Theorem 10). We first consider a preliminary result (Theorem 9).

Let

$$A_n = \sum_{k=0}^{n} a_k \varphi_k(x)$$

be any finite sum of normalized characteristic functions. Consider

$$\mathbf{B}(a_0, a_1, \cdots, a_n) = \int_a^b r(x)[f(x) - A_n(x)]^2\,dx.$$

Then it is easy to show that $\mathbf{B}$ will be a minimum when $a_k = f_k$, $0 \leqq k \leqq n$, where the f_k are given by (3). Thus we conclude:

Theorem 9. Let $f(x)$ be integrable on $[a,b]$ and

$$F_n(x) = \sum_{k=0}^{n} f_k \varphi_k(x)$$

where $f_k = \int_a^b r(x)f(x)\varphi_k(x)\,dx$, $0 \leqq k \leqq n$. Let

$$A_n(x) = \sum_{k=0}^{n} a_k \varphi_k(x)$$

be any finite sum of the normalized characteristic functions $\varphi_k(x)$. Then

$$\int_a^b r(x)[f(x) - F_n(x)]^2\,dx \leqq \int_a^b r(x)[f(x) - A_n(x)]^2\,dx.$$

We now prove our main result.

Theorem 10. Let $f(x)$ be integrable on $[a,b]$. Let

$$F_n(x) = \sum_{k=0}^{n} f_k \, \varphi_k(x)$$

where $f_k = \int_a^b r(x) f(x) \varphi_k(x) \, dx$, $0 \leqq k \leqq n$, and the $\{\varphi_k(x)\}$ are the normalized characteristic functions. Then

$$\lim_{n \to \infty} \int_a^b r(x)[f(x) - F_n(x)]^2 \, dx = 0. \tag{17}$$

Proof. Let $\epsilon > 0$ be assigned. Choose a Sturm function $g(x)$ such that

$$\int_a^b r(x)[f(x) - g(x)]^2 \, dx < \epsilon.$$

Let $\sum_{k=0}^{\infty} g_k \varphi_k(x)$ be the Fourier series associated with $g(x)$. Since $g(x)$ is a Sturm function we may write

$$g(x) = \sum_{k=0}^{\infty} g_k \, \varphi_k(x) \tag{18}$$

by Theorem 7. Let $G_n(x)$ be the nth partial sum of (18). Let

$$f(x) \sim \sum_{k=0}^{\infty} f_k \, \varphi_k(x)$$

and let $F_n(x)$ be the nth partial sum.

By Theorem 8 there exists an N such that

$$\int_a^b r(x)[g(x) - G_n(x)]^2 \, dx < \epsilon$$

for all $n > N$. By Theorem 9,

$$\int_a^b r(x)[f(x) - F_n(x)]^2 \, dx \leqq \int_a^b r(x)[f(x) - G_n(x)]^2 \, dx \tag{19}$$

and

$$\int_a^b r(f-G_n)^2\,dx = \int_a^b r(f-g+g-G_n)^2\,dx$$
$$= \int_a^b r(f-g)^2\,dx + \int_a^b r(g-G_n)^2\,dx + 2\int_a^b r(f-g)(g-G_n)\,dx. \tag{20}$$

From the Cauchy-Schwarz inequality

$$\left[\int_a^b r(f-g)(g-G_n)\,dx\right]^2 \leqq \int_a^b r(f-g)^2\,dx \int_a^b r(g-G_n)^2\,dx.$$

Thus (20) may be written

$$\int_a^b r(f-G_n)^2\,dx \leqq \int_a^b r(f-g)^2\,dx + \int_a^b r(g-G_n)^2\,dx$$
$$+ 2\sqrt{\int_a^b r(f-g)^2\,dx}\sqrt{\int_a^b r(g-G_n)^2\,dx}$$

and if $n > N$,

$$\int_a^b r(f-G_n)^2\,dx < \epsilon + \epsilon + 2\epsilon = 4\epsilon.$$

Thus (19) implies

$$\int_a^b r(x)[f(x) - F_n(x)]^2\,dx < 4\epsilon$$

for all $n > N$ and our theorem is proved.

We shall write (17) as

$$\underset{n\to\infty}{\text{l.i.m.}}\; F_n(x) = f(x)$$

which is read "limit in the mean."

If a set of functions $\{h_n(x) | n = 0, 1, 2, \cdots\}$ is orthonormal on the interval $[c,d]$ with respect to the weighting function $w(x)$ and if $\sum f_k h_k(x)$ is the Fourier series associated with an integrable function

$f(x)$, then we say $\{h_n(x)\}$ is *complete* if

$$\underset{n\to\infty}{\text{l.i.m.}}\ F_n(x) = f(x)$$

where $F_n(x) = \sum_{k=0}^{n} f_k h_k(x)$ and $f_k = \int_c^d w(x) f(x) h_k(x)\, dx$, $k = 0, 1, 2, \cdots, n$. Thus we see that every set of characteristic functions is complete.

Let $f(x)$ be integrable on $[a,b]$ and $\{\varphi_n(x) | n = 0, 1, 2, \cdots\}$ a set of normalized characteristic functions. Then

$$\int_a^b r(x)[f(x) - F_n(x)]^2\, dx$$

$$= \int_a^b r(x)[f^2(x) - 2f(x)F_n(x) + F_n^2(x)]\, dx$$

$$= \int_a^b r(x) f^2(x)\, dx - \sum_{k=0}^{n} f_k^2$$

where $f_k = \int_a^b r(x) f(x) \varphi_k(x)\, dx$, $k = 0, 1, 2, \cdots$. By Theorem 10,

$$\int_a^b r(x) f^2(x)\, dx = \sum_{k=0}^{\infty} f_k^2. \tag{21}$$

Equation (21) is known as *Parseval's equation*. More generally:

Theorem 11. Let $f(x)$ and $g(x)$ be integrable on $[a,b]$, and

$$f(x) \sim \sum_{k=0}^{\infty} f_k\, \varphi_k(x),$$

$$g(x) \sim \sum_{k=0}^{\infty} g_k\, \varphi_k(x)$$

the corresponding Fourier series where the $\{\varphi_n(x) | n = 0, 1, 2, \cdots\}$ are the normalized characteristic functions of the Sturm-Liouville problem (3.1). Then

$$\int_a^b r(x) f(x) g(x)\, dx = \sum_{k=0}^{\infty} f_k g_k.$$

Proof. By hypothesis

$$f(x) + g(x) \sim \sum_{k=0}^{\infty} (f_k + g_k)\, \varphi_k(x)$$

and by (21)

$$\int_a^b r(x)[f(x) + g(x)]^2\, dx = \sum_{k=0}^{\infty} (f_k + g_k)^2.$$

Thus

$$2\int_a^b r(x)f(x)g(x)\, dx = \sum_{k=0}^{\infty} (f_k + g_k)^2 - \sum_{k=0}^{\infty} f_k^2 - \sum_{k=0}^{\infty} g_k^2. \tag{22}$$

Since all three series on the right-hand side of (22) converge (even absolutely), we may write (22) as

$$2\int_a^b r(x)f(x)g(x)\, dx = \sum_{k=0}^{\infty} [(f_k + g_k)^2 - f_k^2 - g_k^2] = 2\sum_{k=0}^{\infty} f_k g_k$$

—which proves our theorem.

6. Fourier Series

The classic example of Sturm-Liouville theory is, of course, *Fourier series*. Consider the special Sturm-Liouville system

$$\begin{aligned} y'' + \lambda y &= 0 \\ y'(0) &= 0 \\ y'(\pi) &= 0. \end{aligned} \tag{1}$$

That is, (1) is a particular case of (3.1) with $p(x) = 1$, $q(x) = 0$, $r(x) = 1$, $a = 0$, $b = \pi$, $\alpha = 0$, $\gamma = 0$. Clearly the (non-normalized) characteristic functions of (1) are

$$\varphi_k^+(x) = \cos kx, \qquad k = 0, 1, 2, \cdots$$

and the corresponding characteristic numbers are

$$\lambda_k^+ = k^2, \qquad k = 0, 1, 2, \cdots.$$

Hence if $f^+(x)$ is a Sturm function defined on $[0,\pi]$, then by Theorem 7,

$$f^+(x) = \sum_{k=0}^{\infty} f_k^+ \cos kx, \qquad x \in [0,\pi] \tag{2}$$

where

$$f_0^+ = \frac{1}{\pi}\int_0^\pi f^+(x)\,dx \tag{3a}$$

$$f_k^+ = \frac{2}{\pi}\int_0^\pi f^+(x)\cos kx\,dx, \qquad k = 1, 2, \cdots. \tag{3b}$$

Furthermore, if $f^+(x)$ is an *even* function defined on $[-\pi,\pi]$, then (2) holds for all $x \in [-\pi,\pi]$.

Now let us consider the Sturm-Liouville system

$$\begin{aligned} y'' + \lambda y &= 0 \\ y(0) &= 0 \\ y(\pi) &= 0. \end{aligned} \tag{4}$$

The (non-normalized) characteristic functions are

$$\varphi_k^-(x) = \sin(k+1)x, \qquad k = 0, 1, 2, \cdots$$

and the corresponding characteristic numbers are

$$\lambda_k^- = (k+1)^2, \qquad k = 0, 1, 2, \cdots.$$

Hence, if $f^-(x)$ is a Sturm function defined on $[0,\pi]$, then by Theorem 7

$$f^-(x) = \sum_{k=0}^{\infty} f_{k+1}^- \sin(k+1)x, \qquad x \in [0,\pi] \tag{5}$$

where

$$f_{k+1}^- = \frac{2}{\pi}\int_0^\pi f^-(x)\sin(k+1)x\,dx, \qquad k = 0, 1, 2, \cdots. \tag{6}$$

Since $\varphi_0^-(0) = 0 = \varphi_0^-(\pi)$ we must have $f^-(0) = 0 = f^-(\pi)$ if $f^-(x)$ is to be a Sturm function. Furthermore, if $f^-(x)$ is an *odd* function defined on $[-\pi,\pi]$, then (5) holds for all $x \in [-\pi,\pi]$.

Equations (2) and (5) establish the half-range Fourier series. We can now state and prove an important result in the theory of Fourier series.

Theorem 12. Let $f(x)$ be continuous and piece-wise differentiable on $[-\pi,\pi]$. Let $f(\pi) = f(-\pi)$. Then the Fourier series

$$\frac{a_0}{2} + \sum_{k=1}^{\infty} (a_k \cos kx + b_k \sin kx)$$

converges uniformly on $[-\pi,\pi]$ to $f(x)$ where

$$a_k = \frac{1}{\pi}\int_{-\pi}^{\pi} f(x) \cos kx \, dx, \qquad k = 0, 1, 2, \cdots \tag{7}$$

$$b_k = \frac{1}{\pi}\int_{-\pi}^{\pi} f(x) \sin kx \, dx, \qquad k = 1, 2, \cdots.$$

Proof. Write

$$f(x) = f^+(x) + f^-(x)$$

where

$$f^+(x) = \frac{f(x) + f(-x)}{2}$$

is an even function of x on $[-\pi,\pi]$ and

$$f^-(x) = \frac{f(x) - f(-x)}{2} \tag{8}$$

is an odd function of x on $[-\pi,\pi]$.

Since $f^+(x)$ is a Sturm function for the Sturm-Liouville system of (1), and furthermore, since it is even, (2) holds for all x in $[-\pi,\pi]$:

$$f^+(x) = \sum_{k=0}^{\infty} f_k^+ \cos kx, \qquad x \in [-\pi,\pi] \tag{9}$$

where the coefficients f_k^+, $k = 0, 1, 2, \cdots$ are given by (3). Similarly, $f^-(x)$ is a Sturm function for the Sturm-Liouville system of (4) since the condition $f(\pi) = f(-\pi)$ implies $f^-(\pi) = 0$ and (8) implies $f^-(0) = 0$. Furthermore, since $f^-(x)$ is an odd function, (5) holds for all x in $[-\pi,\pi]$:

$$f^-(x) = \sum_{k=1}^{\infty} f_k^- \sin kx, \qquad x \in [-\pi,\pi] \tag{10}$$

where the coefficients f_k^-, $k = 1, 2, \cdots$ are given by (6).

Equations (9) and (10) now establish the validity of our theorem provided we can show that

$$\begin{aligned} \tfrac{1}{2}a_0 &= f_0^+ \\ a_k &= f_k^+, \qquad k = 1, 2, \cdots \\ b_k &= f_k^-, \qquad k = 1, 2, \cdots. \end{aligned} \tag{11}$$

But this is an elementary exercise. From (7),

$$\begin{aligned}
\frac{a_0}{2} &= \frac{1}{2\pi}\int_{-\pi}^{\pi} f(x)\,dx \\
&= \frac{1}{2\pi}\int_{-\pi}^{0} f(x)\,dx + \frac{1}{2\pi}\int_{0}^{\pi} f(x)\,dx \\
&= \frac{1}{2\pi}\int_{0}^{\pi} f(-x)\,dx + \frac{1}{2\pi}\int_{0}^{\pi} f(x)\,dx \\
&= \frac{1}{\pi}\int_{0}^{\pi} \frac{1}{2}[f(x) + f(-x)]\,dx \\
&= \frac{1}{\pi}\int_{0}^{\pi} f^{+}(x)\,dx = f_0^{+}
\end{aligned}$$

by (3a), and for $k > 0$,

$$\begin{aligned}
a_k &= \frac{1}{\pi}\int_{-\pi}^{\pi} f(x)\cos kx\,dx \\
&= \frac{1}{\pi}\int_{-\pi}^{0} f(x)\cos kx\,dx + \frac{1}{\pi}\int_{0}^{\pi} f(x)\cos kx\,dx \\
&= \frac{1}{\pi}\int_{0}^{\pi} f(-x)\cos kx\,dx + \frac{1}{\pi}\int_{0}^{\pi} f(x)\cos kx\,dx \\
&= \frac{2}{\pi}\int_{0}^{\pi} f^{+}(x)\cos kx\,dx = f_k^{+}
\end{aligned}$$

by (3b). Similarly we establish (11) and our proof is complete.

8

THE CONSTANT COEFFICIENT CASE

1. Introduction

In preceding chapters we have discussed at some length linear differential equations and their solutions. Thus we know from Chapter 1 that if

$$\mathbf{L} = p_0(x)\frac{d^n}{dx^n} + p_1(x)\frac{d^{n-1}}{dx^{n-1}} + \cdots + p_n(x)\cdot$$

is a linear differential operator where the coefficients $p_i(x)$, $0 \leqq i \leqq n$, are continuous on some closed finite interval I and $p_0(x) > 0$ on I, then there exist n linearly independent functions $\varphi_j(x)$, $1 \leqq j \leqq n$, which have n continuous derivatives on I and which satisfy $\mathbf{L}y = 0$. Knowing that such $\varphi_j(x)$ exist and explicitly finding them, say as elementary functions, or as tabulated functions, or as infinite series, or as integral representations, is indeed another problem.

If $\mathbf{L}$ is of the first order, say

$$\mathbf{L}y \equiv p_0(x)\frac{dy}{dx} + p_1(x)y = 0,$$

then

$$\varphi(x) = y_0 e^{-\int_{x_0}^{x} [p_1(\xi)/p_0(\xi)]d\xi}, \qquad x_0, x \in I$$

is the solution of $\mathbf{L}y = 0$ which assumes the initial value

$$\varphi(x_0) = y_0.$$

However, for $n > 1$, the situation is much different. In fact, even the Sturm-Liouville problems of the preceding chapter which were only of second order are in general not amenable to explicit solution. There are, however, certain classes of great practical interest which can be explicitly solved. We shall discuss some of these in this and the next chapter.

In particular, in this chapter we shall solve linear differential equations with constant coefficients. Consider then

$$\mathbf{L} = a_0 \frac{d^n}{dx^n} + a_1 \frac{d^{n-1}}{dx^{n-1}} + \cdots + a_n.$$

where the a_i, $0 \leqq i \leqq n$, are constants and $a_0 \neq 0$. Then it is well known that if λ is a root of multiplicity r of the algebraic equation

$$a_0\lambda^n + a_1\lambda^{n-1} + \cdots + a_n = 0$$

then

$$\varphi_k(x) = x^{k-1} e^{\lambda x}, \qquad 1 \leqq k \leqq r,$$

are r linearly independent solutions of $\mathbf{L}y = 0$.

Not quite so trivial to solve is the linear differential equation

$$\frac{dY}{dx} = AY \tag{1}$$

where $Y = \{y_1, y_2, \cdots, y_n\}$ us an n-dimensional column vector and $A = \| a_{ij} \|_{1 \leqq i,j \leqq n}$ is a square matrix of constants. Not only do the characteristic roots of A and their multiplicities come into play, but the invariant factors must also be considered. In order to exhibit the solution of (1) explicitly it is convenient to reduce A to some canonical form. Suppose, for example, the characteristic roots λ_i, $1 \leqq i \leqq n$, of the matrix A are all distinct. Then there exists a non-singular $n \times n$ constant matrix P such that

$$P^{-1}AP = N$$

where $N = \| \lambda_i \delta_{ij} \|_{1 \leqq i,j \leqq n}$ is a diagonal matrix of the characteristic roots. If we pre-multiply (1) by P^{-1} and post-multiply by P, then (1) may be written as

$$\frac{d}{dx}(P^{-1}YP) = (P^{-1}AP)(P^{-1}YP)$$

or

$$\frac{dZ}{dx} = NZ \tag{2}$$

where $Z = P^{-1}YP = \{z_1, z_2, \cdots, z_n\}$. The solution of (2) is now trivial. In fact, if x_0 is any real number and $Z_0 = \{z_{10}, z_{20}, \cdots, z_{n0}\}$ is any constant column vector, then

$$Z(x) = \{z_{10}\, e^{\lambda_1(x-x_0)}, z_{20}\, e^{\lambda_2(x-x_0)}, \cdots, z_{n0}\, e^{\lambda_n(x-x_0)}\}$$

is the unique solution of (2), assuming the initial value

$$Z(x_0) = Z_0.$$

For example,

$$\begin{aligned} Z^{(1)}(x) &= \{ e^{\lambda_1(x-x_0)}, & 0\ , & \quad 0\ , & \cdots, & \quad 0 \ \} \\ Z^{(2)}(x) &= \{ \quad 0\ , & e^{\lambda_2(x-x_0)}, & \quad 0\ , & \cdots, & \quad 0 \ \} \\ Z^{(3)}(x) &= \{ \quad 0\ , & 0\ , & e^{\lambda_3(x-x_0)}, & \cdots, & \quad 0 \ \} \\ & \cdot \quad \cdot \quad \cdot & \cdot \quad \cdot & \cdot \quad \cdot & \cdot & \cdot \quad \cdot \\ Z^{(n)}(x) &= \{ \quad 0\ , & 0\ , & \quad 0\ , & \cdots, & e^{\lambda_n(x-x_0)}\} \end{aligned}$$

are n linearly independent vector solutions of (2) and

$$Y^{(i)} = P\, Z^{(i)}\, P^{-1}, \qquad 1 \leqq i \leqq n,$$

are n linearly independent solutions of (1).

The main problem, therefore, is to reduce A to some canonical form. This we shall do in the next three sections where we prove that every square matrix is similar to a matrix in Jordan normal form. Once this important theorem has been proved, we shall return to the problem of constructing explicit solutions of (1). This will be achieved in Section 5.

2. Statement of the Jordan Theorem

In the theory of matrices there exist many important theorems regarding the similarity of matrices. Two square matrices A and B are said to be *similar*, written $A \sim B$, if there exists a non-singular square matrix P such that

$$B = PAP^{-1}.$$

Clearly, similarity is an equivalence relation.

Let n be a fixed positive integer and let $\mathscr{M}$ be the totality of $n \times n$ matrices over the field of complex numbers $\mathscr{K}$. Under the equivalence relation of similarity we can decompose $\mathscr{M}$ into equivalence classes $\mathscr{C}_\iota$ where $\iota \in J$ and J is some index set. That is, if A and B are in the same $\mathscr{C}_\iota$, then $A \sim B$. In each equivalence class $\mathscr{C}_\iota$ choose a representative element. Then the set of these representations is called a *canonical set*. A particular canonical set of great usefulness is the *Jordan set*. We shall determine the form of these Jordan canonical matrices. Precisely, we shall prove the following theorem.

Theorem 1. Let A be an $n \times n$ matrix over the field of complex numbers $\mathscr{K}$. Let $\lambda_1, \lambda_2, \cdots, \lambda_r$ with $r \leqq n$ be the distinct characteristic roots of A. Then there exist r sets of vectors

$$X_0^{(i)}, X_1^{(i)}, \cdots, X_{s_i-1}^{(i)}, \qquad 1 \leqq i \leqq r,$$

with the following properties

(i) $\sum_{i=1}^r s_i = n$.
(ii) The n vectors $X_j^{(i)}$, $1 \leqq i \leqq r$, $0 \leqq j \leqq s_i - 1$ are linearly independent.
(iii) $A X_0^{(i)} = \lambda_i X_0^{(i)}, \qquad 1 \leqq i \leqq r.$
(iv) $A X_j^{(i)} = \epsilon_{ij} X_{j-1}^{(i)} + \lambda_i X_j^{(i)}, \qquad 1 \leqq i \leqq r,\ 1 \leqq j \leqq s_i - 1,$ where ϵ_{ij} is either zero or one.

Thus we see that associated with every matrix A with characteristic roots λ_i, $1 \leqq i \leqq r$, there is a matrix N which can be written as the diagonal partitioned matrix

$$N = \left\| \begin{array}{c:c:c:c:c} R_1 & 0 & 0 & \cdots & 0 \\ \hdashline 0 & R_2 & 0 & \cdots & 0 \\ \hdashline 0 & 0 & R_3 & \cdots & 0 \\ \hdashline \cdot & \cdot & \cdot & \cdot & \cdot \\ \hdashline 0 & 0 & 0 & \cdots & R_m \end{array} \right\| \qquad (1)$$

where each R_k is a square matrix of the form

$$R_k = \begin{Vmatrix} \lambda_i & 1 & 0 & \cdots & 0 & 0 \\ 0 & \lambda_i & 1 & \cdots & 0 & 0 \\ 0 & 0 & \lambda_i & \cdots & 0 & 0 \\ \cdot & \cdot & \cdot & \cdot & \cdot & \cdot \\ 0 & 0 & 0 & \cdots & 0 & \lambda_i \end{Vmatrix}. \tag{2}$$

The matrix R_k has λ_i down its main diagonal, ones down its super-diagonal and zeros elsewhere. Note that more than one R_k can correspond to the same λ_i.

We assert that the matrix A is similar to N. That is, there exists a non-singular square matrix P such that

$$N = P^{-1}AP.$$

By a direct calculation it can be shown that P is a matrix whose columns are the $X_j^{(i)}$ vectors. We call N the *Jordan normal form* of A. Thus every matrix is similar to a matrix in Jordan normal form. No two Jordan matrices are similar, except possibly for a rearrangement of rows and/or columns.

Theorem 1 was worded algebraically. Our proof will be geometric in nature. That is, we shall use the concepts of linear vector spaces. In this language Theorem 1 may be worded as:

Theorem 1′. Let $\mathscr{V}_n$ be an n-dimensional linear vector space over the field of complex numbers $\mathscr{K}$. Let $\mathbf{T}$ be a linear transformation of $\mathscr{V}_n$ into itself. Let $\mathbf{T}$ correspond to a matrix A in some coordinate system. Let $\lambda_1, \lambda_2, \cdots, \lambda_r$, $(r \leqq n)$ be the distinct characteristic roots of $\mathbf{T}$. Then there exist r sets of vectors $X_j^{(i)}$, $1 \leqq i \leqq r, 0 \leqq j \leqq s_i - 1$, with the following properties:

(i) $\sum_{i=1}^{r} s_i = n$.
(ii) The n vectors $X_j^{(i)}$ are linearly independent.
(iii) $\mathbf{T}X_0^{(i)} = \lambda_i X_0^{(i)}$.
(iv) $\mathbf{T}X_j^{(i)} = \epsilon_{ij} X_{j-1}^{(i)} + \lambda_i X_j^{(i)}$ where ϵ_{ij} is either zero or one.

In the above theorem we refer to "some coordinate system." The coordinate system is irrelevant by virtue of the following lemma.

Lemma. The characteristic polynomial of $\mathbf{T}$ is independent of the coordinate system.

Proof. Let $\mathbf{T}$ be a linear transformation over $\mathscr{V}_n$. Let it be represented by A_1 in one coordinate system and by the matrix A_2 in any other coordinate system. Let Y be an arbitrary vector in $\mathscr{V}_n$ which is represented by X_1 in the first coordinate system and by X_2 in the second. Then

$$X_2 = PX_1 \tag{3}$$

where P is a non-singular matrix which depends only on the coordinate systems and not on X_1 or X_2. The vector $\mathbf{T}Y$ is represented by A_1X_1 in the first coordinate system and by A_2X_2 in the second coordinate system. By (3)

$$(A_2X_2) = P(A_1X_1)$$

and

$$A_2X_2 = A_2(PX_1).$$

These two equations imply $A_2P = PA_1$ or

$$A_2 = PA_1P^{-1}. \tag{4}$$

Now in the first coordinate system, the characteristic roots λ of $\mathbf{T}$ are roots of the polynomial equation

$$|A_1 - \lambda E| = 0 \tag{5}$$

where $|A_1 - \lambda E| = \det(A_1 - \lambda E)$ and E is the $n \times n$ identity matrix. In the second coordinate system, the characteristic roots μ of $\mathbf{T}$ are the roots of the polynomial equation

$$|A_2 - \mu E| = 0. \tag{6}$$

From (6) and (4)

$$\begin{aligned} |A_2 - \mu E| &= |PA_1P^{-1} - \mu PP^{-1}| = |P(A_1 - \mu E)P^{-1}| \\ &= |P|\,|A_1 - \mu E|\,|P^{-1}| = |A_1 - \mu E|. \end{aligned}$$

Hence A_1 and A_2 have the same characteristic polynomial.

3. Some Preliminary Lemmas

Let $\mathbf{T}$ be a linear transformation over the n-dimensional vector space $\mathscr{V}_n$. Let $\lambda_1, \lambda_2, \cdots, \lambda_r, (r \leqq n)$ be the distinct characteristic roots of **T**. The main purpose of this section is to show that each λ_i, $1 \leqq i \leqq r$, determines a linear manifold $\mathfrak{M}_i$ such that the $\mathfrak{M}_i$ are mutually disjoint and span the space. This result is stated in Theorem 2 and is preceded by five lemmas. Once having established the theorem, we can reduce our problem to the consideration of a single $\mathfrak{M}_i$, that is, to the problem of determining the canonical form of a matrix which has only one distinct root. The analysis of $\mathfrak{M}_i$ is the crucial part of the theorem and involves an actual construction of the characteristic vectors $X_j^{(i)}$. We shall carry out this portion of the proof in Section 4.

We start our proof of the Jordan theorem by proving the Hamilton-Cayley theorem:

Lemma 1. Every matrix satisfies its own characteristic equation.

Proof. Let A be an $n \times n$ square matrix and let

$$f(\lambda) = |A - \lambda E| \tag{1}$$

be its characteristic polynomial. Since A is a square matrix, the positive integral powers of A are well defined, and hence so is $f(A)$. We shall show that $f(A) \equiv 0$.

Let

$$C(\lambda) = A - \lambda E \tag{2}$$

and let $C^*(\lambda)$ be the adjoint of $C(\lambda)$. That is, if $C(\lambda) = \| c_{ij} \|_{1 \leqq i,j \leqq n}$ and $C^*(\lambda) = \| c_{ij}^* \|_{1 \leqq i,j \leqq n}$, then c_{ij}^* is the cofactor of c_{ji}. Thus

$$C(\lambda)C^*(\lambda) = [\det C(\lambda)]E = f(\lambda)E. \tag{3}$$

Now, explicitly,

$$f(A) = (-1)^n A^n + a_1 A^{n-1} + \cdots + a_n E \tag{4}$$

and

$$f(\lambda)E = (-1)^n(\lambda E)^n + a_1(\lambda E)^{n-1} + \cdots + a_n E. \tag{5}$$

Subtract (5) from (4):

$$f(A) - f(\lambda)E = (-1)^n[A^n - (\lambda E)^n] + a_1[A^{n-1} - (\lambda E)^{n-1}] + \cdots + a_{n-1}(A - \lambda E).$$

Since E is the identity matrix and λ and the a_i are scalars (that is, complex numbers) we may write, by virtue of commutativity, that

$$\begin{aligned} f(A) - f(\lambda)E &= (A-\lambda E)(-1)^n[A^{n-1} + \lambda A^{n-2} + \cdots + \lambda^{n-1}E] \\ &\quad + a_1(A-\lambda E)[A^{n-2} + \lambda A^{n-3} + \cdots + \lambda^{n-2}E] \\ &\quad + \cdots \\ &\quad + a_{n-1}(A-\lambda E) \\ &= \text{(say) } (A-\lambda E)D(\lambda). \end{aligned}$$

Therefore

$$\begin{aligned} f(A) &= f(\lambda)E + (A-\lambda E)D(\lambda) \\ &= (A-\lambda E)[C^*(\lambda) + D(\lambda)] \end{aligned} \tag{6}$$

by (3) and (2). If $C^*(\lambda) + D(\lambda) \not\equiv 0$, then the expression on the right-hand side of (6) would effectively involve λ. But $f(A)$ is independent of λ. Thus $C^*(\lambda) + D(\lambda) \equiv 0$ and therefore $f(A) \equiv 0$.

Lemma 2. Let $p(x)$ and $q(x)$ be relatively prime polynomials in the ring of polynomials $\mathscr{K}[x]$ over the complex field $\mathscr{K}$. Let A be a square matrix. Then there exist polynomials $\varphi(x)$ and $\psi(x)$ in $\mathscr{K}[x]$ such that

$$\varphi(A)p(A) + \psi(A)q(A) = E. \tag{7}$$

Proof. Since $\mathscr{K}[x]$ is a Euclidean ring without divisors of zero we may invoke the Euclidean algorithm to show the existence of polynomials $\varphi(x)$ and $\psi(x)$ in $\mathscr{K}[x]$ such that

$$\varphi(x)p(x) + \psi(x)q(x) = 1. \tag{8}$$

Now (8) depends only on a certain relation among the coefficients of the polynomials p, q, φ and ψ. These facts and the commutativity of powers of A establish (7).

Lemma 3. Let A be a square matrix and λ_i a characteristic root of multiplicity s_i. Then there exists a linear manifold $\mathfrak{M}_i$ generated by vectors X which have the property that

$$(A-\lambda_i E)^{s_i} X = 0.$$

Proof. For each λ_i there is at least one characteristic vector X_i. That is, there exists a non-zero vector X_i such that

$$(A-\lambda_i E)X_i = 0.$$

Thus $(A-\lambda_i E)^k X_i = 0$ for any positive integer k, and in particular

$$(A-\lambda_i E)^{s_i} X_i = 0.$$

We are endeavoring to reduce our problem to one in which we have just one characteristic root. Toward this end we shall prove (cf. Theorem 2) that every $X \in \mathscr{V}_n$ can be uniquely expressed as a sum

$$X = X_1 + X_2 + \cdots + X_r$$

where $X_i \in \mathfrak{M}_i$. Note that this implies that the $\mathfrak{M}_i$ are pair-wise disjoint and that $\mathscr{V}_n$ is the direct sum of the $\mathfrak{M}_i$ Thus, as we discussed in the introductory paragraph of this section, we can concentrate on the structure of just one $\mathfrak{M}_i$. There still remain, however, two more simple lemmas that we must prove.

Lemma 4. If $X \in \mathfrak{M}_i$, then $AX \in \mathfrak{M}_i$.

Proof. Since $X \in \mathfrak{M}_i$, we have $(A-\lambda_i E)^{s_i} X = 0$ by Lemma 3. Now $A(A-\lambda_i E)^{s_i} X = (A-\lambda_i E)^{s_i} AX$ since A and $A-\lambda_i E$ commute. Hence $(AX) \in \mathfrak{M}_i$.

Suppose now that λ is any complex number in $\mathscr{K}$ and X any vector in $\mathfrak{M}_i$. Then λX, AX, and $AX-\lambda X$ are in $\mathfrak{M}_i$. Thus the linear transformation $A-\lambda E$ takes $\mathfrak{M}_i$ into itself. Indeed, any polynomial $p(A)$ takes $\mathfrak{M}_i$ into itself. Furthermore, we assert that $A-\lambda E$ must have an inverse on $\mathfrak{M}_i$ for $\lambda \neq \lambda_i$. More generally we shall prove the following result:

Lemma 5. Let $\mathfrak{M}_i$ be as above, m any positive integer and λ any complex number unequal to λ_i. Let X be any vector in $\mathfrak{M}_i$. Then there exists a vector Y in $\mathfrak{M}_i$ such that

$$X = (A-\lambda E)^m Y. \tag{9}$$

Proof. Let X be any vector in $\mathfrak{M}_i$ and let

$$p(A) = (A-\lambda_i E)^{s_i}$$
$$q(A) = (A-\lambda E)^m.$$

Since $\lambda \neq \lambda_i$, the polynomials p and q are relatively prime. By Lemma 2 there exist polynomials φ and ψ such that

$$\varphi(A)p(A) + \psi(A)q(A) = E.$$

But for $X \in \mathfrak{M}_i$ we have $p(A)X = 0$ by Lemma 4. Therefore

$$\psi(A)q(A)X = X.$$

Since any polynomial in A takes $\mathfrak{M}_i$ into itself, the transformations $\psi(A)$ and $q(A)$ are inverses of each other on $\mathfrak{M}_i$. Thus given X, define Y by $\psi(A)X = Y$. Then

$$X = q(A)[\psi(A)X] = q(A)Y = (A-\lambda E)^m Y$$

since $q(A)$ and $\psi(A)$ commute.

We are now prepared to prove the main result of this section.

Theorem 2. Every $X \in \mathscr{V}_n$ may be uniquely expressed as a sum

$$X = X_1 + X_2 + \cdots + X_r$$

where $X_i \in \mathfrak{M}_i$, $1 \leqq i \leqq r$.

Proof. By Lemma 1, $f(A) \equiv 0$ where $f(\lambda) = |A - \lambda E|$ is the characteristic polynomial of A. Therefore

$$f(A)X = (-1)^n A^n X + a_1 A^{n-1} X + \cdots + a_n EX \equiv 0 \tag{10}$$

for all $X \in \mathscr{V}_n$. Since $f(\lambda)$ is a polynomial it can be factored, say

$$f(\lambda) = (-1)^n(\lambda-\lambda_1)^{s_1}(\lambda-\lambda_2)^{s_2}\cdots(\lambda-\lambda_r)^{s_r}$$

where s_i is the multiplicity of the zero λ_i. The commutativity of the powers of A again enable us to write (10) as

$$(A-\lambda_1 E)^{s_1}(A-\lambda_2 E)^{s_2}\cdots(A-\lambda_r E)^{s_r} X \equiv 0 \tag{11}$$

for every $X \in \mathscr{V}_n$. We may therefore write

$$(A-\lambda_1 E)^{s_1}[(A-\lambda_2 E)^{s_2}\cdots(A-\lambda_r E)^{s_r} X] \equiv 0. \tag{12}$$

Let Y_1 be the vector in brackets in (12). That is,

$$Y_1 = (A-\lambda_2 E)^{s_2}\cdots(A-\lambda_r E)^{s_r} X. \tag{13}$$

By Lemma 5 we know that $(A-\lambda_2 E)^{s_2}$ has an inverse on $\mathfrak{M}_1$ since $\lambda_2 \neq \lambda_1$. That is, there exists a $Y_1' \in \mathfrak{M}_1$ such that

$$(A-\lambda_2 E)^{s_2} Y_1' = Y_1. \tag{14}$$

Subtracting (13) from (14) we obtain

$$0 = (A-\lambda_2 E)^{s_2}[Y_1' - (A-\lambda_3 E)^{s_3}\cdots(A-\lambda_r E)^{s_r} X].$$

Call $-Y_2'$ the term in brackets in the above equation. Then $Y_2' \in \mathfrak{M}_2$ and

$$Y_1' + Y_2' = (A-\lambda_3E)^{s_3} \cdots (A-\lambda_rE)^{s_r}X. \tag{15}$$

Since $(A-\lambda_3E)^{s_3}$ has an inverse on $\mathfrak{M}_1$ and $\mathfrak{M}_2$, there exist vectors $Y_1'' \in \mathfrak{M}_1$ and $Y_2'' \in \mathfrak{M}_2$ such that $(A-\lambda_3E)^{s_3}Y_1'' = Y_1'$ and $(A-\lambda_3E)^{s_3}Y_2'' = Y_2'$. Thus

$$(A-\lambda_3E)^{s_3}(Y_1'' + Y_2'') = Y_1' + Y_2'. \tag{16}$$

Subtracting (15) from (16) results in

$$0 = (A-\lambda_3E)^{s_3}[Y_1'' + Y_2'' - (A-\lambda_4E)^{s_4} \cdots (A-\lambda_rE)^{s_r}X].$$

Call $-Y_3''$ the term in brackets in the above equation. Then $Y_3'' \in \mathfrak{M}_3$ and

$$Y_1'' + Y_2'' + Y_3'' = (A-\lambda_4E)^{s_4} \cdots (A-\lambda_rE)^{s_r}X.$$

Continuing this process until we reach X, we see that X may be expressed in the form

$$X = X_1 + X_2 + \cdots + X_r \tag{17}$$

where $X_i \in \mathfrak{M}_i$, $1 \leqq i \leqq r$.

To prove uniqueness let us suppose that X may also be represented by

$$X = X_1' + X_2' + \cdots + X_r' \tag{18}$$

with $X_i' \in \mathfrak{M}_i$, $1 \leqq i \leqq r$. Subtracting (18) from (17) we obtain

$$0 = (X_1 - X_1') + (X_2 - X_2') + \cdots + (X_r - X_r')$$

or

$$\Delta_1 + \Delta_2 + \cdots + \Delta_r = 0 \tag{19}$$

where $\Delta_i = X_i - X_i' \in \mathfrak{M}_i$, $1 \leqq i \leqq r$.

Now $(A-\lambda_1E)^{s_1}$ and $(A-\lambda_2E)^{s_2} \cdots (A-\lambda_rE)^{s_r}$, considered as polynomials in A, are relatively prime. Hence there exist polynomials φ and ψ such that

$$\varphi(A)(A-\lambda_1E)^{s_1} + \psi(A)[(A-\lambda_2E)^{s_2} \cdots (A-\lambda_rE)^{s_r}] = E. \tag{20}$$

Suppose $\Delta_1 \neq 0$. Then $E\Delta_1 \neq 0$. But

$$(A-\lambda_1E)^{s_1}\Delta_1 = 0$$

since $\Delta_1 \in \mathfrak{M}_1$. Also $\Delta_1 = -\Delta_2 - \Delta_3 - \cdots - \Delta_r$ by (19) and

$$(A-\lambda_2 E)^{s_2}\cdots(A-\lambda_r E)^{s_r}(-\Delta_2-\Delta_3-\cdots-\Delta_r) = 0$$

since $(A-\lambda_i E)^{s_i}$ and $(A-\lambda_j E)^{s_j}$ commute and $\Delta_i \in \mathfrak{M}_i$, $2 \leqq i \leqq r$. Hence (20) implies

$$E\Delta_1 = 0$$

which contradicts the assumption that $\Delta_1 \neq 0$. Thus $\Delta_1 = 0$. Similarly we conclude that $\Delta_i = 0$, $2 \leqq i \leqq r$. The representation (17) is therefore unique.

4. Proof of the Jordan Theorem

As before, let **T** be a linear transformation over the n-dimensional vector space $\mathscr{V}_n$ and $\lambda_1, \lambda_2, \cdots, \lambda_r$, $(r \leqq n)$ the distinct characteristic roots of **T**. Let $\mathfrak{M}_i$, $1 \leqq i \leqq r$, be the disjoint manifolds previously constructed. Let t_i be the dimension of $\mathfrak{M}_i$ and $W_j^{(i)}$, $1 \leqq j \leqq t_i$, a linearly independent set of vectors which span $\mathfrak{M}_i$. Since the space $\mathscr{V}_n$ is the direct sum of the $\mathfrak{M}_i$, the vectors $W_j^{(i)}$, $1 \leqq i \leqq r$, $1 \leqq j \leqq t_i$, form a basis for $\mathscr{V}_n$. Let A be the matrix corresponding to the linear transformation **T** in this coordinate system. More explicitly, since $AW_j^{(i)}$ is in $\mathfrak{M}_i$ for $1 \leqq j \leqq t_i$, we may write

$$AW_j^{(i)} = \sum_{k=1}^{t_i} a_{jk}^{(i)} W_k^{(i)}, \qquad 1 \leqq i \leqq r,\ 1 \leqq j \leqq t_i.$$

Thus the matrix A is a partitioned diagonal matrix whose diagonal terms are the matrices $A^{(i)}$ and $A^{(i)}$ is the transpose of $\| a_{jk}^{(i)} \|_{1 \leqq j,k \leqq t_i}$, $1 \leqq i \leqq r$.

Our earlier arguments (Lemma 5 of the preceding section) have shown that $(A-\lambda E)^m$ has an inverse on $\mathfrak{M}_i$ if $\lambda \neq \lambda_i$. Consequently the matrix $A^{(i)}$ cannot have a characteristic root other than λ_i. Since $(A-\lambda_i E)^{s_i} \equiv 0$ on $\mathfrak{M}_i$ we conclude that λ_i is a characteristic root. Thus $t_i = s_i$, that is, the dimension of $\mathfrak{M}_i$ is s_i. Now if we confine our attention to the boxes $A^{(i)}$ and show that for each of these we can find vectors $X_j^{(i)}$ which have the properties enounced in Theorem 1, then we shall have proved the Jordan theorem. But we have now reduced our problem to the case where the matrix to be considered has only one characteristic root λ_i. Furthermore, if we consider $A^{(i)} - \lambda_i E^{(i)}$

(where $E^{(i)}$ is the $s_i \times s_i$ identity matrix) rather than $A^{(i)}$ we can assume that this only characteristic root has the value zero. One can readily verify that if the result holds for $A^{(i)} - \lambda_i E^{(i)}$, it holds also for $A^{(i)}$.

To simplify the notation, and without loss of generality, let us assume that B is an $m \times m$ matrix whose only characteristic root is zero. Then the characteristic equation of B must be of the form

$$\lambda^m = 0.$$

By Lemma 1 of the preceding section we must have $B^m \equiv 0$. Now let q be the smallest positive integer such that $B^q \equiv 0$. For $p \leqq q$ let $\mathfrak{N}_p$ be the linear manifold determined by vectors Y such that $B^p Y = 0$. Clearly

$$\{0\} = \mathfrak{N}_0 \subset \mathfrak{N}_1 \subset \mathfrak{N}_2 \subset \cdots \subset \mathfrak{N}_q = \mathscr{V}_m$$

where $\mathscr{V}_m$ is the m-dimensional vector space itself.

Let $\mathfrak{M}_1 = \mathfrak{N}_q \ominus \mathfrak{N}_{q-1}$; that is, $\mathfrak{M}_1$ is perpendicular to the null-space of B^{q-1}, and indeed to the null-space of B^s for $1 \leqq s < q$. Let $X_1^{(1)}$, $X_2^{(1)}, \cdots, X_{k_1}^{(1)}$ be a basis in $\mathfrak{M}_1$. The vectors $BX_j^{(1)}$, $1 \leqq j \leqq k_1$, are in $\mathfrak{N}_{q-1}$ since $B^{q-1}(BX_j^{(1)}) = B^q X_j^{(1)}$ and $B^q \equiv 0$. We also assert that the $BX_j^{(1)}$ are linearly independent relative to $\mathfrak{N}_{q-2}$. That is, if $\sum_{j=1}^{k_1} c_j BX_j^{(1)}$ is in $\mathfrak{N}_{q-2}$ we must have $c_j = 0$, $1 \leqq j \leqq k_1$.

Proof. Suppose $\sum_j c_j BX_j^{(1)} \in \mathfrak{N}_{q-2}$. Since $B^{q-2}Y = 0$ if $Y \in \mathfrak{N}_{q-2}$ we must have

$$0 = B^{q-2}\Big(\sum_j c_j BX_j^{(1)}\Big) = B^{q-1}\Big(\sum_j c_j X_j^{(1)}\Big).$$

But this equation implies $\sum_j c_j X_j^{(1)} \in \mathfrak{N}_{q-1}$; and since $\sum_j c_j X_j^{(1)}$ is also in $\mathfrak{M}_1$ we must have $\sum_j c_j X_j^{(1)} = 0$. The linear independence of the $X_j^{(1)}$ implies $c_j = 0$, $1 \leqq j \leqq k_1$.

In brief: $BX_j^{(1)} \in \mathfrak{N}_{q-1}$ and $BX_j^{(1)} \notin \mathfrak{N}_{q-2}$ for $1 \leqq j \leqq k_1$. Now it may be that $BX_j^{(1)}$, $1 \leqq j \leqq k_1$, and $\mathfrak{N}_{q-2}$ determine $\mathfrak{N}_{q-1}$. In this case let $\mathfrak{M}_2 = \{0\}$. Otherwise let $\mathfrak{M}_2$ consist of those elements of $\mathfrak{N}_{q-1}$ which are perpendicular to $BX_j^{(1)}$, $1 \leqq j \leqq k_1$, and to $\mathfrak{N}_{q-2}$ (the null-space of B^{q-2}). Let $X_j^{(2)}$, $1 \leqq j \leqq k_2$, be a basis in $\mathfrak{M}_2$. In general, let $\mathfrak{M}_s$ denote the set of vectors in $\mathfrak{N}_{q-s+1}$, $2 \leqq s \leqq q$, perpendicular to $B^{s-1}X_j^{(1)}$, $1 \leqq j \leqq k_1$; $B^{s-2}X_j^{(2)}$, $1 \leqq j \leqq k_2$; $\cdots$; $BX_j^{(s-1)}$, $1 \leqq j \leqq k_{s-1}$, (all of which are in $\mathfrak{N}_{q-s+1}$) and to $\mathfrak{N}_{q-s}$. And if $\mathfrak{M}_s$ is not $\{0\}$, let $X_j^{(s)}$, $1 \leqq j \leqq k_s$, be a basis in $\mathfrak{M}_s$. Reference to Fig. 3 may prove helpful.

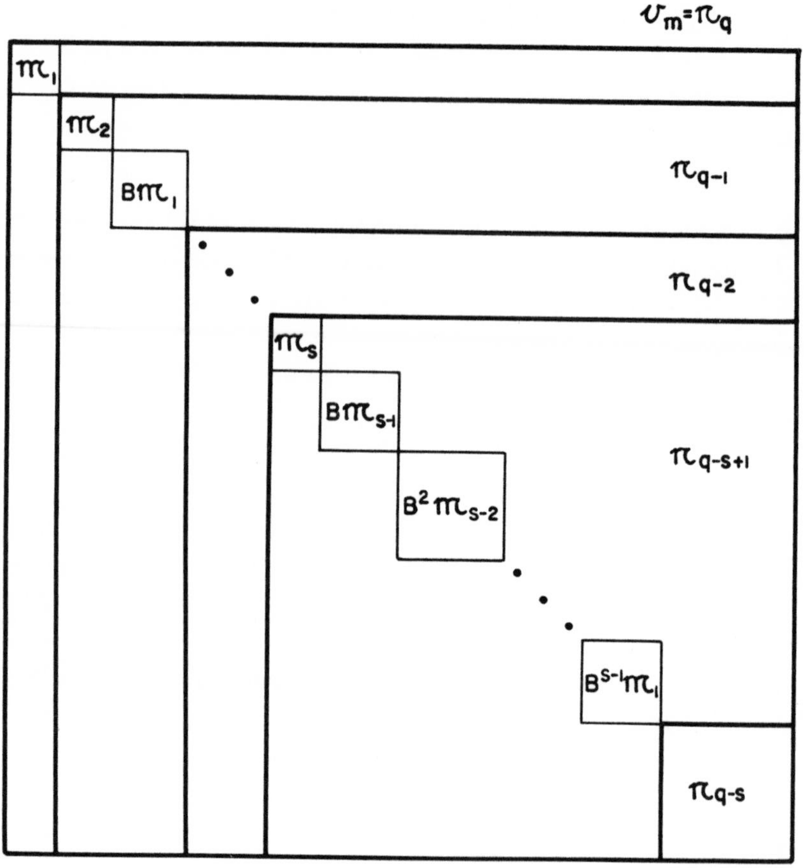

Fig. 3

We shall now prove that the vectors

$$B^{s-i}X_j^{(i)}, \qquad 1 \leqq i \leqq s-1, \qquad 1 \leqq j \leqq k_i, \tag{1}$$

are linearly independent relative to $\mathfrak{N}_{q-s}$. Using this fact, we can then show that the vectors

$$B^v X_j^{(u)}, \qquad 1 \leqq u \leqq q, \qquad 0 \leqq v \leqq q-u, \qquad 1 \leqq j \leqq k_u \tag{2}$$

are linearly independent.

Suppose for the moment that the above results have been established. We assert that the vectors of (2) span $\mathscr{V}_m$. For the introduction of the $X_j^{(s)}$ assured us that $\mathfrak{N}_{q-s+1}$ was spanned provided that $\mathfrak{N}_{q-s}$ was spanned. The final step is for $s = q$, and thus $\mathfrak{N}_1$ is spanned since $\mathfrak{N}_0 = \{0\}$. Thus the $B^v X_j^{(u)}$ vectors constitute a basis for $\mathscr{V}_m$.

For fixed s and j let

$$Z_u = B^{q-s-u} X_j^{(s)}, \qquad 0 \leqq u \leqq q - s.$$

Now $X_j^{(s)} \in \mathfrak{M}_s \subset \mathfrak{N}_{q-s+1}$. Consequently

$$0 = B^{q-s+1} X_j^{(s)} = B(B^{q-s} X_j^{(s)}) = BZ_0$$

while

$$BZ_u = B^{q-s-(u-1)} X_j^{(s)} = Z_{u-1}, \qquad 1 \leqq u \leqq q - s.$$

Thus in the manifold spanned by the Z_u, $0 \leqq u \leqq q - s$, B is determined by a $(q-s+1) \times (q-s+1)$ matrix with ones down the superdiagonal and zeros everywhere else:

$$\left\| \begin{matrix} 0 & 1 & 0 & \cdots & 0 & 0 \\ 0 & 0 & 1 & \cdots & 0 & 0 \\ 0 & 0 & 0 & \cdots & 0 & 0 \\ . & . & . & . & . & . \\ 0 & 0 & 0 & \cdots & 0 & 1 \\ 0 & 0 & 0 & \cdots & 0 & 0 \end{matrix} \right\| . \tag{3}$$

Since the $B^v X_j^{(u)}$ constitute a basis for $\mathscr{V}_m$ we may define such sets of Z vectors as above so that a matrix similar to B consists of boxes such as (3) strung along the diagonal, and zeros elsewhere. This completes the proof of the theorem.

It remains but to prove the contentions regarding (1) and (2). We first note that if $BY \in \mathfrak{N}_{q-s}$, then $Y \in \mathfrak{N}_{q-s+1}$.

Proof. $BY \in \mathfrak{N}_{q-s}$ implies $0 = B^{q-s}(BY) = B^{q-s+1} Y$ and hence $Y \in \mathfrak{N}_{q-s+1}$.

We prove (1) inductively on s. Suppose that c_{ij} are constants such that

$$Z = \sum_{i=1}^{s-1} \sum_{j=1}^{k_i} c_{ij} B^{s-i} X_j^{(i)}$$

is in $\mathfrak{N}_{q-s}$. Let

$$W = \sum_{i=1}^{s-2} \sum_{j=1}^{k_i} c_{ij} B^{s-i-1} X_j^{(i)} + \sum_{j=1}^{k_{s-1}} c_{s-1,j} X_j^{(s-1)}.$$

Then $BW = Z$ and $W \in \mathfrak{N}_{q-s+1}$. Now by construction the $X_j^{(s-1)}$ are orthogonal to $B^{s-i-1}X_j^{(i)}$ and in $\mathfrak{M}_{s-1}$ ($\subset \mathfrak{N}_{q-s+2}$). But $\mathfrak{M}_{s-1}$ is orthogonal to $\mathfrak{N}_{q-s+1}$. Thus the $c_{s-1,j}$ are zero and

$$W = \sum_{i=1}^{s-2} \sum_{j=1}^{k_i} c_{ij} B^{s-i-1} X_j^{(i)}$$

is in $\mathfrak{N}_{q-s+1}$. But the hypothesis of our induction implies that $c_{ij} = 0$, $1 \leqq i \leqq s-2$, $1 \leqq j \leqq k_i$. Consequently all the c_{ij} are zero.

To establish the linear independence of the vectors of (2) on $\mathscr{V}_m = \mathfrak{N}_q$ we shall assume the contrary and force a contradiction. Let $c_{\nu uj}$ be constants not all zero such that

$$\sum_{u=1}^{q} \sum_{\nu=0}^{q-u} \sum_{j=1}^{k_u} c_{\nu uj} B^{\nu} X_j^{(u)} = 0. \tag{4}$$

Make the change of variable $s = u + \nu$ in the above sum. Then we may write (4) as

$$\sum_{s=1}^{q} \sum_{u=1}^{s} \sum_{j=1}^{k_u} c_{s-u,u,j} B^{s-u} X_j^{(u)} = 0. \tag{5}$$

Now let σ be the largest value of s such that some $c_{\sigma-u,u,j} \neq 0$. Then (5) may be written

$$\sum_{s=1}^{\sigma-1} \sum_{u=1}^{s} \sum_{j=1}^{k_u} c_{s-u,u,j} B^{s-u} X_j^{(u)} + \sum_{u=1}^{\sigma} \sum_{j=1}^{k_u} c_{\sigma-u,u,j} B^{\sigma-u} X_j^{(u)} = 0$$

or

$$\sum_{s=1}^{\sigma-1} \sum_{u=1}^{s} \sum_{j} c_{s-u,u,j} B^{s-u} X_j^{(u)} = -\sum_{u=1}^{\sigma} \sum_{j} c_{\sigma-u,u,j} B^{\sigma-u} X_j^{(u)}. \tag{6}$$

Now $B^{s-u}X_j^{(u)} \in \mathfrak{N}_{q-s+1}$ for $s < \sigma$ and $1 \leqq u \leqq s$. (The case $u = s$ yields $X_j^{(s)}$ or $\mathfrak{M}_s$ which of course is in $\mathfrak{N}_{q-s+1}$.) Hence by (1) *no* such $B^{s-u}X_j^{(u)}$ is in $\mathfrak{N}_{q-\sigma+1}$. But the $B^{\sigma-u}X_j^{(u)}$ *are* in $\mathfrak{N}_{q-\sigma+1}$. (The case $u = \sigma$ yields $X_j^{(\sigma)}$ or $\mathfrak{M}_\sigma$ which is in $\mathfrak{N}_{q-\sigma+1}$.) Thus from (6)

$$\sum_{u=1}^{\sigma} \sum_{j=1}^{k_u} c_{\sigma-u,u,j} B^{\sigma-u} X_j^{(u)} = 0.$$

Another application of (1) implies the $c_{\sigma - u,u,j} = 0$—a contradiction. The linear independence of the set of vectors of (2) has thus been established.

5. Solution in Matrix Form

Consider the differential equation

$$\frac{dY}{dx} = AY \tag{1}$$

where $Y(x) = \{y_1(x), y_2(x), \cdots, y_n(x)\}$ is an n-dimensional column vector and $A = \| a_{ij} \|_{1 \leqq i,j \leqq n}$ is a square matrix of constants. Let N be the Jordan normal form of A. Then if

$$N = P^{-1}AP$$

we may write (1) as

$$\frac{dZ}{dx} = NZ \tag{2}$$

where $Z = P^{-1}YP$.

Let us consider a typical block

$$R = \begin{Vmatrix} \lambda & 1 & 0 & \cdots & 0 & 0 \\ 0 & \lambda & 1 & \cdots & 0 & 0 \\ 0 & 0 & \lambda & \cdots & 0 & 0 \\ \cdot & \cdot & \cdot & \cdot & \cdot & \cdot \\ 0 & 0 & 0 & \cdots & \lambda & 1 \\ 0 & 0 & 0 & \cdots & 0 & \lambda \end{Vmatrix}$$

of N [cf. (2.1) and (2.2)] of dimension s, and the differential equation

$$\frac{dV}{dx} = RV \tag{3}$$

where $V(x) = \{v_1(x), v_2(x), \cdots, v_s(x)\}$. Let x_0 be any real number and $V_0 = \{v_{10}, v_{20}, \cdots, v_{s0}\}$ be any constant vector. We shall first solve (3) with the initial condition V_0 at x_0, and then relate it to the solutions of (2) and (1).

In scalar form we may write (3) as

$$\begin{aligned}
\frac{dv_1}{dx} &= \lambda v_1 + v_2 \\
\frac{dv_2}{dx} &= \lambda v_2 + v_3 \\
&\cdots\cdots\cdots \\
\frac{dv_{s-1}}{dx} &= \lambda v_{s-1} + v_s \\
\frac{dv_s}{dx} &= \lambda v_s.
\end{aligned} \tag{4}$$

The solution of

$$\frac{dv_s}{dx} = \lambda v_s$$

with the initial condition $v_s(x_0) = v_{s0}$ is

$$v_s(x) = v_{s0}\, e^{\lambda(x-x_0)}. \tag{5}$$

The solution of

$$\frac{dv_{s-1}}{dx} = \lambda v_{s-1} + v_s \tag{6}$$

can now be obtained by replacing v_s by its explicit representation (5) and rewriting (6) as

$$\frac{dv_{s-1}}{dx} - \lambda v_{s-1} = v_{s0}\, e^{\lambda(x-x_0)}.$$

The solution of the above equation with the initial value $v_{s-1}(x_0) = v_{s-1,0}$ is

$$v_{s-1}(x) = [v_{s0}(x-x_0) + v_{s-1,0}]\, e^{\lambda(x-x_0)}$$

and in general

$$v_{s-k}(x) = \left[v_{s0}\frac{(x-x_0)^k}{k!} + v_{s-1,0}\frac{(x-x_0)^{k-1}}{(k-1)!} + \cdots + v_{s-k,0}\right]e^{\lambda(x-x_0)}, \quad 0 \leqq k \leqq s-1. \tag{7}$$

Thus

$$V(x) = \{v_1(x), v_2(x), \cdots, v_s(x)\}$$

where the $v_j(x)$ are given by (7) is the unique solution of (3) assuming the initial value

$$V(x_0) = V_0.$$

If, without loss of generality, we let $x_0 = 0$ and

$$V_0^{(k)} = \{\delta_{k1}, \delta_{k2}, \cdots, \delta_{ks}\}, \qquad 1 \leqq k \leqq s,$$

then

$$\begin{aligned}
V^{(1)}(x) &= \{\ 1, \ 0, \ \ldots, \ 0, \ 0, \ 0\}\, e^{\lambda x} \\
V^{(2)}(x) &= \{\ x, \ 1, \ \cdots, \ 0, \ 0, \ 0\}\, e^{\lambda x} \\
V^{(3)}(x) &= \{\ \frac{x^2}{2}, \ x, \ \cdots, \ 0, \ 0, \ 0\}\, e^{\lambda x} \\
&\cdot \quad \cdot \quad \cdot \quad \cdot \quad \cdot \quad \cdot \quad \cdot \\
V^{(s-1)}(x) &= \{\frac{x^{s-2}}{(s-2)!}, \frac{x^{s-3}}{(s-3)!}, \ \cdots, \ x, \ 1, \ 0\}\, e^{\lambda x} \\
V^{(s)}(x) &= \{\frac{x^{s-1}}{(s-1)!}, \frac{x^{s-2}}{(s-2)!}, \ \cdots, \ \frac{x^2}{2}, \ x, \ 1\}\, e^{\lambda x}
\end{aligned} \tag{8}$$

are s linearly independent solutions of (3).

If the block R contains the $\beta+1, \beta+2, \cdots, \beta+s$ rows and columns of N, then

$$Z^{(\beta+k)}(x) = \{0_\beta, V^{(k)}(x), 0_{n-\beta-s}\}, \qquad 1 \leqq k \leqq s,$$

[where 0_β and $0_{n-\beta-s}$ are zero vectors of dimensions β and $n-\beta-s$ respectively and the $V^{(k)}(x)$ are given by (8)] provide s linearly independent solutions of (2).

If each of the m blocks R_k, $1 \leqq k \leqq m$, of (2.1) is treated in a similar fashion, we obtain the requisite n linearly independent vector solutions $Z^{(j)}(x)$, $1 \leqq j \leqq n$, of (2). Of course

$$Y^{(j)} = PZ^{(j)}P^{-1}, \qquad 1 \leqq j \leqq n,$$

are the desired solutions of (1).

For example if

$$N_6 = \left\| \begin{array}{c|ccc|cc}
\lambda & 0 & 0 & 0 & 0 & 0 \\ \hline
0 & \lambda & 1 & 0 & 0 & 0 \\
0 & 0 & \lambda & 1 & 0 & 0 \\
0 & 0 & 0 & \lambda & 0 & 0 \\ \hline
0 & 0 & 0 & 0 & \mu & 1 \\
0 & 0 & 0 & 0 & 0 & \mu
\end{array} \right\|,$$

then

$$\begin{aligned}
Z^{(1)}(x) &= \{1 \;\vdots\; 0, \; 0, \; 0 \;\vdots\; 0, \; 0\}\, e^{\lambda x} \\
Z^{(2)}(x) &= \{0 \;\vdots\; 1, \; 0, \; 0 \;\vdots\; 0, \; 0\}\, e^{\lambda x} \\
Z^{(3)}(x) &= \{0 \;\vdots\; x, \; 1, \; 0 \;\vdots\; 0, \; 0\}\, e^{\lambda x} \\
Z^{(4)}(x) &= \{0 \;\vdots\; \frac{x^2}{2}, \; x, \; 1 \;\vdots\; 0, \; 0\}\, e^{\lambda x} \\
Z^{(5)}(x) &= \{0 \;\vdots\; 0, \; 0, \; 0 \;\vdots\; 1, \; 0\}\, e^{\mu x} \\
Z^{(6)}(x) &= \{0 \;\vdots\; 0, \; 0, \; 0 \;\vdots\; x, \; 1\}\, e^{\mu x}
\end{aligned}$$

are six linearly independent solutions of

$$\frac{dZ}{dX} = N_6 Z.$$

9

INFINITE SERIES REPRESENTATIONS

1. Introduction

We saw in the last chapter that explicit solutions of our basic differential equation

$$\mathbf{L}y \equiv p_0(x)y^{(n)} + p_1(x)y^{(n-1)} + \cdots + p_n(x)y = 0 \qquad (1)$$

could be constructed provided the $p_i(x)$, $0 \leqq i \leqq n$, were constants. This suggests that if additional restrictions (other than continuity) are placed on the $p_i(x)$, perhaps we can also obtain explicit solutions of (1). For example, suppose $p_i(x) \in C^m(I)$ and $p_0(x) > 0$ on I where I is some closed finite interval. Our basic existence and uniqueness theorem of Chapter 1 guarantees the existence of n linearly independent solutions $\varphi_j(x)$, $1 \leqq j \leqq n$, each of which has n continuous derivatives on I. However, from the identity

$$\varphi_j^{(n)}(x) \equiv -\frac{p_1(x)}{p_0(x)}\varphi_j^{(n-1)}(x) - \frac{p_2(x)}{p_0(x)}\varphi_j^{(n-2)}(x) - \cdots - \frac{p_n(x)}{p_0(x)}\varphi_j(x)$$

we can also conclude that $\varphi_j(x) \in C^{n+m}(I)$. It seems reasonable, therefore, that if the $p_i(x)$ are analytic on I, then the solutions will also be analytic. If this be the case, then the $\varphi_j(x)$ may be expressed as power series with positive radii of convergence. We shall exploit this point of view in the next section.

2. The Method of Frobenius

A differential equation of the form

$$(x-a)^n\frac{d^ny}{dx^n}+(x-a)^{n-1}q_1(x)\frac{d^{n-1}y}{dx^{n-1}} + (x-a)^{n-2}q_2(x)\frac{d^{n-2}y}{dx^{n-2}}+\cdots+q_n(x)y = 0, \tag{1}$$

where the $q_i(x)$, $1 \leqq i \leqq n$, are analytic in a neighborhood of $x=a$, is said to have a *regular singularity* at $x=a$. Of course, equation (1) of the preceding section when the $p_i(x)$ are analytic and $p_0(x)>0$ is a special case of the above equation. We shall show by the *method of Frobenius* how to obtain solutions of (1) in a neighborhood of $x=a$. A more complete discussion of singularities of differential equations is best studied in the complex domain and will not be presented here.

With no loss of generality, let $a=0$ in (1) and with little loss of generality, let $n=2$. Thus we shall consider

$$\mathbf{L}y \equiv x^2\frac{d^2y}{dx^2}+x\,p(x)\frac{dy}{dx}+q(x)\,y = 0 \tag{2}$$

where $p(x)$ and $q(x)$ are analytic in a neighborhood of the origin. Note that most of the important equations of mathematical physics are subsumed under (2). It will be convenient to assume that x is complex-valued, although this fact will be rarely used. After a complete discussion of (2), it should be clear how our results could be generalized to include (1).

The method of Frobenius assumes that the solution of (2) may be expressed in the form

$$y(x,s) = \sum_{n=0}^{\infty} a_n\, x^{n+s}, \qquad a_0 \neq 0, \tag{3}$$

where s and the coefficients a_n are to be determined so that (3) is formally a solution of (2). (The convergence of the power series will be established in the next section.)

Since $p(x)$ and $q(x)$ are analytic in a neighborhood of the origin we may express them as convergent power series:

$$p(x) = \sum_{m=0}^{\infty}\alpha_m x^m \qquad \text{and} \qquad q(x) = \sum_{m=0}^{\infty}\beta_m x^m \tag{4}$$

respectively. Substituting (3) and (4) in (2) and collecting powers of x, we obtain

$$\mathbf{L}y(x,s) = \sum_{p=0}^{\infty} \{a_p[(p+s)(p+s-1) + (p+s)\alpha_0 + \beta_0] + \sum_{q=0}^{p-1} a_q[(q+s)\alpha_{p-q} + \beta_{p-q}]\}x^{p+s}. \tag{5}$$

Now introduce the functions

$$\begin{aligned} f_0(s) &= s(s-1) + s\alpha_0 + \beta_0 \\ f_r(s) &= s\alpha_r + \beta_r, \qquad r = 1, 2, \cdots. \end{aligned} \tag{6}$$

Then (5) becomes

$$\mathbf{L}y(x,s) = \sum_{p=0}^{\infty} [a_p f_0(p+s) + \sum_{q=0}^{p-1} a_q f_{p-q}(q+s)]x^{p+s}. \tag{7}$$

If $\mathbf{L}y(x,s)$ is to equal zero we must have

$$\begin{aligned} &a_0 f_0(s) = 0 \\ &a_1 f_0(s+1) + a_0 f_1(s) = 0 \\ &a_2 f_0(s+2) + a_1 f_1(s+1) + a_0 f_2(s) = 0 \\ &\cdot \quad \cdot \quad \cdot \quad \cdot \quad \cdot \quad \cdot \quad \cdot \quad \cdot \\ &a_p f_0(s+p) + a_{p-1} f_1(s+p-1) + \cdots + a_0 f_p(s) = 0 \\ &\cdot \quad \cdot \quad \cdot \quad \cdot \quad \cdot \quad \cdot \quad \cdot \quad \cdot \quad \cdot \quad \cdot \end{aligned} \tag{8}$$

Since $a_0 \neq 0$, we must have

$$f_0(s) = 0$$

if the first of equations (8) is to be satisfied. We call $f_0(s) = 0$ the *indicial* equation. Since

$$f_0(s) = s(s-1) + s\alpha_0 + \beta_0 = (s-s_1)(s-s_2),$$

the indicial equation determines two values of s, namely, s_1 and s_2, which may or may not be distinct. Choose a value of s such that $f_0(s+\nu) \neq 0$ for $\nu = 1, 2, \cdots$. Then

$$a_1(s) = -a_0 \frac{f_1(s)}{f_0(s+1)}$$

$$a_2(s) = -a_0 \frac{[f_0(s+1)f_2(s) - f_1(s)f_1(s+1)]}{f_0(s+1)f_0(s+2)}$$

and in general

$$a_n(s) = a_0 \frac{F_n(s)}{G_n(s)} \tag{9}$$

where

$$F_n(s) = (-1)^n \begin{vmatrix} f_1(s) & f_0(s+1) & 0 & \cdots & 0 \\ f_2(s) & f_1(s+1) & f_0(s+2) & \cdots & 0 \\ \cdot & \cdot & \cdot & \cdot & \cdot \\ f_{n-1}(s) & f_{n-2}(s+1) & f_{n-3}(s+2) & \cdots & f_0(s+n-1) \\ f_n(s) & f_{n-1}(s+1) & f_{n-2}(s+2) & \cdots & f_1(s+n-1) \end{vmatrix} \tag{10}$$

and

$$G_n(s) = f_0(s+1)\, f_0(s+2) \cdots f_0(s+n). \tag{11}$$

If s_1 and s_2 do not differ by an integer, then $f_0(s_1+\nu) \neq 0, f_0(s_2+\nu) \neq 0$ for ν a positive integer. For suppose $f_0(s_1+\nu) = 0$. Then $s_1+\nu$ must equal s_1 or s_2. Since $\nu > 0$, $s_1+\nu \neq s_1$ and since s_1-s_2 is not an integer, $s_1+\nu \neq s_2$. Similarly, $f_0(s_2+\nu) \neq 0$ for any positive integer ν. Thus

$$a_n(s_1) \qquad \text{and} \qquad a_n(s_2)$$

form the coefficients of two distinct series $y(x,s_1)$ and $y(x,s_2)$. Assuming for the moment that the series converge, we have obtained a fundamental system of solutions.

To treat the exceptional cases where s_1 and s_2 are equal or differ by an integer, we consider a parameter σ whose variation is restricted to a neighborhood of s_1 or s_2 and is so small that $G_n(\sigma) \neq 0$. Consider the series

$$y(x,\sigma) = \sum_{n=0}^{\infty} a_n\, x^{n+\sigma} \tag{12}$$

where a_0 is arbitrary but the other a_n satisfy the recurrence relations of (8) except for the first one. Then

$$\mathbf{L}y(x,\sigma) = a_0 f_0(\sigma) x^{\sigma}. \tag{13}$$

The previous solutions are now obtained by taking $\sigma = s_1$ or s_2.

Consider now the case where $s_1 = s_2$. Then $f_0(\sigma) = (\sigma - s_1)^2$. One solution, $y(x,s_1)$, is still obtained by setting $\sigma = s_1$ in (13). To determine the second solution, we have from (13), assuming $x > 0$,

$$\frac{\partial}{\partial\sigma}\mathbf{L}y(x,\sigma) = \mathbf{L}\frac{\partial}{\partial\sigma}y(x,\sigma) = a_0 f_0'(\sigma)x^\sigma + a_0 f_0(\sigma)x^\sigma \log x$$

and

$$\mathbf{L}\frac{\partial}{\partial\sigma}y(x,s_1) = 0$$

since s_1 is a root of $f_0'(\sigma) = 0$ as well as of $f_0(\sigma) = 0$. The cummutativity of $\mathbf{L}$ and $\partial/\partial\sigma$ will follow when we prove in the next section that

$$\sum_{k=0}^{\infty} a_k(\sigma)\, x^k$$

converges uniformly in σ.

Thus we see that

$$\hat{y}(x,s_1) = \frac{\partial}{\partial\sigma}y(x,s_1)$$

is a solution of (2). To determine this solution explicitly we write

$$\begin{aligned}\frac{\partial}{\partial\sigma}y(x,\sigma) &= \frac{\partial}{\partial\sigma}\sum_{n=0}^{\infty} a_n(\sigma)\, x^{n+\sigma}\\ &= (\log x)\sum_{n=0}^{\infty} a_n(\sigma)\, x^{n+\sigma} + \sum_{n=0}^{\infty}\frac{\partial}{\partial\sigma}a_n(\sigma)\, x^{n+\sigma}\end{aligned}$$

and

$$\begin{aligned}\hat{y}(x,s_1) &= (\log x)\sum_{n=0}^{\infty} a_n(s_1)\, x^{n+s_1} + \sum_{n=0}^{\infty}\frac{\partial}{\partial\sigma}a_n(s_1)\, x^{n+s_1}\\ &= (\log x)\, y(x,s_1) + \sum_{n=0}^{\infty}\frac{\partial}{\partial\sigma}a_n(s_1)\, x^{n+s_1}. \qquad (14)\end{aligned}$$

Finally consider the case where $s_1 - s_2 = k$, a positive integer. Let $y(x,s_1)$ be as before. Clearly it is determined since $G_n(s_1) = f_0(s_1+1)f_0(s_1+2)\cdots f_0(s_1+n) \neq 0$ since $s_1 + \nu \neq s_2$ for ν a positive integer. (Recall that $s_1 > s_2$). Thus we still have one solution. Consider now

$$\begin{aligned}y^*(x,\sigma) &= (\sigma - s_2)y(x,\sigma)\\ &= (\sigma - s_2)\sum_{n=0}^{\infty} a_n(\sigma)\, x^{n+\sigma} \qquad (15)\\ &= \sum_{n=0}^{\infty} b_n(\sigma)\, x^{n+\sigma}\end{aligned}$$

where $b_n(\sigma) = (\sigma - s_2)\, a_n(\sigma)$. Then

$$b_n(\sigma) = (\sigma - s_2)\, a_n(\sigma) = (\sigma - s_2)\, a_0 \frac{F_n(\sigma)}{G_n(\sigma)} \tag{16}$$

and all $b_n(s_2) = 0$ for $0 \leqq n \leqq k - 1$.

But for $n \geqq k$,

$$G_n(s_2) = f_0(s_2+1)\, f_0(s_2+2) \cdots f_0(s_2+k) \cdots f_0(s_2+n) \tag{17}$$

and $s_2 + k = s_1$. Thus $f_0(s_2+k) = f_0(s_1) = 0$ since s_1 is a root of the indicial equation, and $G_n(s_2) = 0$. But of course the factor $(\sigma - s_2)$ in the numerator of (16) also vanishes for $\sigma = s_2$.

We proceed to treat this case. From (10), for $m = 0, 1, 2, \cdots$ we may write the determinant $F_{m+k}(s_2)$ as shown on page 177 opposite. But $f_0(s_2+k) = f_0(s_1) = 0$. Thus by the Laplace development

$$\begin{aligned} F_{m+k}(s_2) &= (-1)^{m+k}[(-1)^{-k}\, F_k(s_2)\, (-1)^{-m}\, F_m(s_2+k)] \\ &= F_k(s_2)\, F_m(s_1). \end{aligned} \tag{18}$$

Also

$$\begin{aligned} &G_{m+k}(\sigma) \\ &= f_0(\sigma+1) f_0(\sigma+2) \cdots f_0(\sigma+k-1) f_0(\sigma+k) f_0(\sigma+k+1) \cdots f_0(\sigma+m+k) \\ &= G_{k-1}(\sigma)\, f_0(\sigma+k)\, G_m(\sigma+k). \end{aligned} \tag{19}$$

Further we recall that

$$\begin{aligned} f_0(\sigma) &= (\sigma - s_1)(\sigma - s_2) \\ f_0(\sigma+k) &= (\sigma+k-s_1)(\sigma+k-s_2) = (\sigma - s_2)(\sigma+k-s_2). \end{aligned}$$

Thus

$$\begin{aligned} b_{m+k}(\sigma) &= (\sigma - s_2)\, a_{m+k}(\sigma) = (\sigma - s_2)\, a_0 \frac{F_{m+k}(\sigma)}{G_{m+k}(\sigma)} \\ &= \frac{a_0(\sigma - s_2)\, F_{m+k}(\sigma)}{G_{k-1}(\sigma)\, (\sigma - s_2)(\sigma+k-s_2) G_m(\sigma+k)} \\ &= \frac{a_0\, F_{m+k}(\sigma)}{G_{k-1}(\sigma)\, (\sigma+k-s_2)\, G_m(\sigma+k)} \end{aligned}$$

and

$$b_{m+k}(s_2) = \frac{F_k(s_2)}{k\, G_{k-1}(s_2)}\, a_m(s_1). \tag{20}$$

$$F_{m+k}(s_2) = (-1)^{m+k} \begin{vmatrix} f_1(s_2) & f_0(s_2+1) & 0 & \cdots & 0 & 0 & 0 & \cdots & 0 \\ f_2(s_2) & f_1(s_2+1) & f_0(s_2+2) & \cdots & 0 & 0 & 0 & \cdots & 0 \\ \cdot & \cdot & \cdot & \cdot & \cdot & \cdot & \cdot & \cdot & \cdot \\ f_k(s_2) & f_{k-1}(s_2+1) & f_{k-2}(s_2+2) & \cdots & f_1(s_2+k-1) & f_0(s_2+k) & 0 & \cdots & 0 \\ f_{k+1}(s_2) & f_k(s_2+1) & f_{k-1}(s_2+2) & \cdots & f_2(s_2+k-1) & f_1(s_2+k) & f_0(s_2+k+1) & \cdots & 0 \\ \cdot & \cdot & \cdot & \cdot & \cdot & \cdot & \cdot & \cdot & \cdot \\ f_{k+m}(s_2) & f_{k+m-1}(s_2+1) & f_{k+m-2}(s_2+2) & \cdots & f_{m+1}(s_2+k-1) & f_m(s_2+k) & f_{m-1}(s_2+k+1) & \cdots & f_1(s_2+m+k-1) \end{vmatrix}$$

Since $b_n(s_2) = 0$ for $0 \leqq n \leqq k-1$,

$$y^*(x,s_2) = \sum_{n=0}^{\infty} b_n(s_2)\, x^{n+s_2} = \sum_{n=k}^{\infty} b_n(s_2)\, x^{n+s_2}$$

$$= \sum_{m=0}^{\infty} b_{m+k}(s_2)\, x^{m+k+s_2} = A \sum_{m=0}^{\infty} a_m(s_1)\, x^{m+s_1}$$

$$= A\, y(x,s_1)$$

where

$$A = \frac{F_k(s_2)}{k\, G_{k-1}(s_2)}. \tag{21}$$

Thus $y^*(x,s_2)$ is just a constant multiple of $y(x,s_1)$.

To obtain the second solution in this case, we write, for $x > 0$,

$$\frac{\partial}{\partial \sigma} \mathbf{L} y^*(x,\sigma) = \frac{\partial}{\partial \sigma}[(\sigma - s_2) a_0 f_0(\sigma)\, x^\sigma]$$

$$= a_0[f_0(\sigma)\, x^\sigma + (\sigma - s_2) f_0'(\sigma)\, x^\sigma + (\sigma - s_2) f_0(\sigma)(\log x)\, x^\sigma]$$

and

$$\mathbf{L} \frac{\partial}{\partial \sigma} y^*(x,\sigma) \Big|_{\sigma = s_2} = 0. \tag{22}$$

Explicitly

$$\frac{\partial}{\partial \sigma} y^*(x,\sigma) = (\log x) \sum_{n=0}^{\infty} b_n(\sigma)\, x^{n+\sigma} + \sum_{n=0}^{\infty} \frac{\partial}{\partial \sigma} b_n(\sigma)\, x^{n+\sigma}$$

$$= (\log x)\, y^*(x,\sigma) + \sum_{n=0}^{\infty} c_n(\sigma)\, x^{n+\sigma}$$

where

$$c_n(\sigma) = \frac{\partial}{\partial \sigma} b_n(\sigma). \tag{23}$$

Thus

$$\begin{aligned} \bar{y}(x,s_2) &= \frac{\partial}{\partial \sigma} y^*(x,s_2) = (\log x)\, y^*(x,s_2) + \sum_{n=0}^{\infty} c_n(s_2)\, x^{n+s_2} \\ &= (\log x)\, A\, y(x,s_1) + \sum_{n=0}^{\infty} c_n(s_2)\, x^{n+s_2}. \end{aligned} \tag{24}$$

Clearly $y(x,s_1)$ and $\bar{y}(x,s_2)$ are linearly independent if $A \neq 0$. Now suppose $A = 0$. We assert that the two solutions are still linearly independent. For suppose the contrary. Then $\sum_{n=0}^{\infty} c_n(s_2)x^{n+s_2}$ would have to be a constant multiple of $\sum_{n=0}^{\infty} a_n(s_1)x^{n+s_1}$. In particular, since $a_0 \neq 0$

$$y(x,s_1) = a_0\, x^{s_1} + \cdots$$

and this implies

$$c_0(s_2) = c_1(s_2) = \cdots = c_{k-1}(s_2) = 0.$$

But

$$c_0(s) = \frac{\partial}{\partial s}\, b_0(s) = \frac{\partial}{\partial s}\,(s-s_2)a_0 = a_0$$

and

$$c_0(s_2) = a_0 \neq 0$$

—a contradiction.

3. Convergence of the Development

Let σ be a parameter whose range of variation is restricted to a neighborhood of s_1 or s_2. To be concrete, let

$$|\sigma - s_i| \leqq \tfrac{1}{2} \min\,(1, |s_1 - s_2|), \qquad i = 1, 2. \tag{1}$$

Now

$$p(x) = \sum_{k=0}^{\infty} \alpha_k x^k, \qquad q(x) = \sum_{k=0}^{\infty} \beta_k x^k$$

are analytic in a neighborhood of $x=0$. Let $R > 0$ be less than the minimum of the radii of convergence of $p(x)$ and $q(x)$. Then if σ satisfies (1), there exists a constant M, independent of k and σ such that

$$|f_k(\sigma+r)|\, R^k = |[(\sigma+r)\alpha_k + \beta_k]R^k| < M(r+1) \tag{2}$$

for $k=1, 2, \cdots$ and $r=0, 1, 2, \cdots$. Since s_1 and s_2 are the only roots of $f_0(s)=0$ and since σ is restricted by (1), we can find an integer N such that

$$f_0(\sigma+r) \neq 0$$

for $r \geqq N$.

Now from (2.8)

$$a_r(\sigma) = -\frac{1}{f_0(\sigma+r)} \sum_{k=1}^{r} a_{r-k}\, f_k(\sigma+r-k).$$

Since the $a_r(\sigma)$ are rational functions of σ and $f_0(\sigma+r) \neq 0$ for $r \geqq N$, we conclude that the $a_r(\sigma)$ are analytic functions of σ. From (2),

$$|f_k(\sigma+r)| < \frac{M(r+1)}{R^k}, \qquad k = 1, 2, \cdots$$

and thus

$$|a_r(\sigma)| < \frac{M}{|f_0(\sigma+r)|}\sum_{k=1}^{r} |a_{r-k}| \frac{(r-k+1)}{R^k}. \tag{3}$$

Call A_r the right-hand side of the inequality of (3). Then

$$|a_r(\sigma)| < A_r, \qquad r \geqq N \tag{4}$$

and

$$A_{r+1} = \frac{M}{|f_0(\sigma+r+1)|\, R}\left[\frac{A_r|f_0(\sigma+r)|}{M} + |a_r|(r+1)\right]$$

or

$$\frac{A_{r+1}}{A_r} = \frac{|f_0(\sigma+r)|}{R\,|f_0(\sigma+r+1)|} + \frac{M\,(r+1)\,|a_r|}{R\,|f_0(\sigma+r+1)|\,A_r}.$$

By (4) we may conclude

$$\frac{A_{r+1}}{A_r} < \frac{|f_0(\sigma+r)|}{R\,|f_0(\sigma+r+1)|} + \frac{M\,(r+1)}{R\,|f_0(\sigma+r+1)|}.$$

But

$$\lim_{r\to\infty} \frac{r+1}{|f_0(\sigma+r+1)|} = 0 \tag{5}$$

and

$$\lim_{r\to\infty} \frac{|f_0(\sigma+r)|}{|f_0(\sigma+r+1)|} = 1. \tag{6}$$

Thus

$$\lim_{r\to\infty} \frac{A_{r+1}}{A_r} \leqq \frac{1}{R}$$

and

$$\sum_{k=N}^{\infty} A_k\, x^k$$

converges for $|x| < R$.

But

$$|a_r| < A_r, \qquad r = N, N+1, \cdots$$

by (4). The radius of convergence of

$$\sum_{r=0}^{\infty} a_r(\sigma)\, x^r \tag{7}$$

is therefore not less than R. Since the limits of (5) and (6) are uniform with respect to σ, the convergence of (7) is uniform in σ.

4. An Example

Before continuing further, let us consider a numerical example of the method of Frobenius. The differential equation

$$x^2y'' + xy' - (x^2+\nu^2)y = 0 \tag{1}$$

is known as the *modified Bessel equation of order* ν. Since $x=0$ is a regular singular point we may apply the method of Frobenius.

In the notation of Section 2,

$$p(x) = 1$$

and

$$q(x) = -\nu^2 - x^2$$

[cf. (2.2)]. And from (2.6) the indicial polynomial is

$$f_0(s) = s^2 - \nu^2. \tag{2}$$

Thus the zeros of $f_0(s)$ are

$$s_1 = \nu, \qquad s_2 = -\nu.$$

(There is no loss of generality in assuming $\nu \geqq 0$. We shall do so.) Again from (2.6)

$$\begin{aligned} f_1(s) &= 0 \\ f_2(s) &= -1 \\ f_r(s) &= 0, \qquad r \geqq 3. \end{aligned} \tag{3}$$

Equations (2.8) then become in this case

$$\begin{aligned} a_0(s-\nu)(s+\nu) &= 0 \\ a_1(s-\nu+1)(s+\nu+1) &= 0 \\ a_r(s-\nu+r)(s+\nu+r) - a_{r-2} &= 0, \qquad r \geqq 2 \end{aligned} \tag{4}$$

and

$$a_{2p}(\sigma) = \frac{a_0}{[(\sigma-\nu+2)(\sigma-\nu+4)\cdots(\sigma-\nu+2p)][(\sigma+\nu+2)(\sigma+\nu+4)\cdots(\sigma+\nu+2p)]}. \tag{5}$$

Thus from (5)

$$a_{2p}(s_1) = a_{2p}(\nu) = \frac{a_0\,\Gamma(\nu+1)}{2^{2p}\,p!\,\Gamma(\nu+p+1)}, \qquad p = 0, 1, 2, \cdots \tag{6}$$

where $\Gamma(u)$ is the Gamma function. We also conclude from (4) that

$$a_{2p+1}(s_1) = 0, \qquad p = 0, 1, 2, \cdots.$$

Hence

$$y(x,s_1) = \sum_{p=0}^{\infty} a_{2p}(s_1)\,x^{2p+s_1}$$

$$= \Gamma(\nu+1)\,2^{\nu}\,a_0 \sum_{p=0}^{\infty} \frac{1}{\Gamma(\nu+p+1)p!}\left(\frac{x}{2}\right)^{2p+\nu}. \tag{7}$$

If we let $a_0 = [2^{\nu}\,\Gamma(\nu+1)]^{-1}$, the resulting function

$$I_\nu(x) = \sum_{p=0}^{\infty} \frac{1}{\Gamma(\nu+p+1)p!}\left(\frac{x}{2}\right)^{2p+\nu} \tag{8}$$

is known as the *modified Bessel function of the first kind and order* ν.

If $s_1 - s_2 = \nu - (-\nu) = 2\nu$ is not an integer, a second solution is obtained by replacing ν by $-\nu$ in (8), viz.:

$$I_{-\nu}(x) = \sum_{p=0}^{\infty} \frac{1}{\Gamma(p-\nu+1)p!}\left(\frac{x}{2}\right)^{2p-\nu}. \tag{9}$$

Suppose now that the roots of the indicial equation differ by an integer; that is, 2ν is an integer. We distinguish three cases:

(i) $\nu = 0$.

(ii) ν is a half integer.

(iii) ν is an integer.

Case (ii) is the easiest to dispose of. Since the roots differ by an integer we must refer to (2.24). In this case it is easy to see that $A = 0$ [cf. (2.21)]. By definition [cf. (2.23) and (2.16)]

$$c_n(\sigma) = \frac{\partial}{\partial\sigma} b_n(\sigma) = \frac{\partial}{\partial\sigma} (\sigma - s_2)\, a_n(\sigma).$$

But [cf. (5)], the factor $(\sigma + \nu)$ does not cancel. Thus

$$\frac{\partial}{\partial\sigma} (\sigma+\nu)\, a_{2p}(\sigma) = (\sigma+\nu)\frac{\partial}{\partial\sigma} a_{2p}(\sigma) + a_{2p}(\sigma)$$

and

$$c_{2p}(s_2) = c_{2p}(-\nu) = a_{2p}(-\nu).$$

The second solution of (1) is therefore given by

$$\begin{aligned}\bar{y}(x,s_2) &= \sum_{p=0}^{\infty} c_{2p}(s_2)\, x^{2p+s_2} \\ &= y(x,s_2) = \sum_{p=0}^{\infty} a_{2p}(s_2)\, x^{2p+s_2} \\ &= \sum_{p=0}^{\infty} a_{2p}(-\nu)\, x^{2p-\nu}.\end{aligned}$$

Now from (5)

$$a_{2p}(-\nu) = \frac{a_0\Gamma(1-\nu)}{2^{2p}\Gamma(p-\nu+1)\, p!}$$

and hence

$$\begin{aligned}y(x,s_2) = y(x,-\nu) &= a_0 2^{-\nu}\Gamma(1-\nu)\sum_{p=0}^{\infty}\frac{1}{\Gamma(p-\nu+1)\, p!}\left(\frac{x}{2}\right)^{2p-\nu} \qquad (10)\\ &= a_0 2^{-\nu}\Gamma(1-\nu) I_{-\nu}(x)\end{aligned}$$

--which leads to (9). It is easy to see that (7) and (10) are linearly independent. Thus, as long as ν is not an integer, we obtain the two linearly independent solutions $I_\nu(x)$ and $I_{-\nu}(x)$ of (1).

Let us now consider case (i), that is, $\nu = 0$. From (5)

$$a_{2p}(\sigma) = \frac{a_0}{[(\sigma+2)(\sigma+4)\cdots(\sigma+2p)]^2},$$

and

$$\begin{aligned}\frac{\partial}{\partial\sigma} a_{2p}(\sigma) &= a_{2p}(\sigma)\frac{\partial}{\partial\sigma}\log a_{2p}(\sigma) \\ &= -2a_{2p}(\sigma)\sum_{k=1}^{p}\frac{1}{\sigma+2k}.\end{aligned}$$

Since $s_1 = \nu = 0$,

$$\frac{\partial}{\partial\sigma}\log a_{2p}(0) = -\sum_{k=1}^{p}\frac{1}{k} = -[\psi(p+1) + \gamma]$$

where

$$\psi(n+1) = 1 + \frac{1}{2} + \frac{1}{3} + \cdots + \frac{1}{n} - \gamma$$

$$\psi(1) = -\gamma$$

and γ is Euler's constant. Thus

$$\frac{\partial}{\partial\sigma}a_{2p}(\sigma)\bigg|_{\sigma=0} = -\frac{a_0}{2^{2p}p!p!}[\psi(p+1) + \gamma].$$

Now from (2.14) and (7)

$$\hat{y}(x,s_1) = (\log x)\, a_0\, I_0(x) - a_0\sum_{p=0}^{\infty}\frac{1}{p!p!}[\psi(p+1) + \gamma]\left(\frac{x}{2}\right)^{2p}.$$

If we add $a_0 I_0(x)[\gamma - \log 2]$ to the above expression and then let $a_0 = -1$, we obtain

$$K_0(x) = -I_0(x)\log\frac{x}{2} + \sum_{p=0}^{\infty}\frac{\psi(p+1)}{p!p!}\left(\frac{x}{2}\right)^{2p} \tag{11}$$

as the second linearly independent solution of (1) with $\nu = 0$. We call $K_0(x)$ the *modified Bessel function of the second kind and order zero.*

We now turn to the difficult case (iii) where ν is an integer. Equation (2.24) must be invoked, and we must compute A and the $c_n'(s_2)$. From (2.21)

$$A = \frac{F_{2\nu}(-\nu)}{(2\nu)G_{2\nu-1}(-\nu)}$$

and from (2.10) and (2.11)

$$F_{2\nu}(\sigma) = f_0(\sigma+1)\, f_0(\sigma+3)\, f_0(\sigma+5) \cdots f_0(\sigma+2\nu-1)$$

$$G_{2\nu-1}(\sigma) = f_0(\sigma+1)\, f_0(\sigma+2)\, f_0(\sigma+3) \cdots f_0(\sigma+2\nu-1).$$

Hence

$$A = \frac{1}{(2\nu)f_0(2-\nu)f_0(4-\nu)\cdots f_0(\nu-2)} = \frac{(-1)^{\nu-1}}{2^{2\nu-1}\nu!(\nu-1)!}. \tag{12}$$

To compute the c_n we first note that

$$a_{2p}(\sigma) = a_0, \qquad p = 0$$

$$a_{2p}(\sigma) = \frac{a_0}{[(\sigma-\nu+2)(\sigma-\nu+4)\cdots(\sigma-\nu+2p)][(\sigma+\nu+2)(\sigma+\nu+4)\cdots(\sigma+\nu+2p)]}, \quad 0<p<\nu,$$

$$a_{2p}(\sigma) = \frac{a_0}{(\sigma-\nu+2)(\sigma-\nu+4)\cdots(\sigma+\nu)(\sigma+\nu+2)\cdots(\sigma+\nu+2p)}, \quad p=\nu,$$

$$a_{2p}(\sigma) = \frac{a_0}{[(\sigma-\nu+2)(\sigma-\nu+4)\cdots(\sigma+\nu-2)(\sigma+\nu)][(\sigma+\nu+2)(\sigma+\nu+4)\cdots(\sigma+2p-\nu)]^2 [(\sigma+2p-\nu+2)(\sigma+2p-\nu+4)\cdots(\sigma+2p+\nu)]}, \quad p>\nu.$$

Since

$$c_{2p}(\sigma) = \frac{\partial}{\partial\sigma} b_{2p}(\sigma)$$

where $b_{2p}(\sigma) = (\sigma - s_2)\, a_{2p}(\sigma) = (\sigma+\nu)\, a_{2p}(\sigma)$ we obtain, with the aid of logarithmic differentiation,

$$c_{2p}(-\nu) = \frac{a_0\,(-1)^p\,(\nu-p-1)!}{2^{2p}\,(\nu-1)!\,p!}, \qquad p<\nu,$$

$$c_{2p}(-\nu) = \frac{-a_0\,(-1)^{\nu-1}}{2^{2p}\,(\nu-1)!(p-\nu)!p!}[\psi(p-\nu+1)+\psi(p+1)-\psi(\nu)+\gamma], \quad p \geqq \nu. \tag{13}$$

Thus, again from (2.24),

$$\bar{y}(x,s_2) = A\,(\log x) y(x,s_1) + \sum_{n=0}^{\infty} c_n(s_2)\, x^{n+s_2}$$
$$= \frac{a_0(-1)^{\nu-1}}{2^{\nu-1}\,(\nu-1)!} I_\nu(x)\log x + \sum_{p=0}^{\infty} c_{2p}(-\nu)\, x^{2p-\nu}$$

by (12), (7) and (8). And from (13)

$$\bar{y}(x,-\nu) = \frac{a_0\,(-1)^{\nu-1}}{2^{\nu-1}(\nu-1)!} I_\nu(x)\log x$$
$$+ \frac{a_0}{2^\nu(\nu-1)!}\sum_{p=0}^{\nu-1}\frac{(-1)^p(\nu-p-1)!}{p!}\left(\frac{x}{2}\right)^{2p-\nu}$$
$$+ \frac{a_0(-1)^\nu}{2^\nu\,(\nu-1)!}\sum_{p=\nu}^{\infty}\frac{1}{(p-\nu)!p!}[\psi(p-\nu+1)+\psi(p+1)-\psi(\nu)+\gamma]\left(\frac{x}{2}\right)^{2p-\nu}.$$

Now make the change of dummy index $p - \nu = m$ in the last sum of the above equation. Then

$$\bar{y}(x, -\nu) = \frac{a_0}{2^{\nu-1}(\nu-1)!}\Bigg[(-1)^{\nu-1} I_\nu(x)\log x$$

$$+ \frac{1}{2}\sum_{p=0}^{\nu-1} \frac{(-1)^p(\nu-p-1)!}{p!}\left(\frac{x}{2}\right)^{2p-\nu}$$

$$+ \frac{(-1)^\nu}{2}\sum_{m=0}^{\infty}\frac{1}{m!(m+\nu)!}[\psi(m+1) + \psi(m+\nu+1) - \psi(\nu) + \gamma]\left(\frac{x}{2}\right)^{2m+\nu}\Bigg].$$

If we let $a_0 = [2^{\nu-1}(\nu-1)!]$ and then add $(-1)^\nu I_\nu(x)\,[\log 2 + \frac{1}{2}\psi(\nu) - \frac{1}{2}\gamma]$ to the above expression, we obtain

$$K_\nu(x) = (-1)^{\nu-1} I_\nu(x)\log\frac{x}{2} + \frac{1}{2}\sum_{p=0}^{\nu-1}\frac{(-1)^p(\nu-p-1)!}{p!}\left(\frac{x}{2}\right)^{2p-\nu}$$

$$+ \frac{(-1)^\nu}{2}\sum_{m=0}^{\infty}\frac{1}{m!(m+\nu)!}[\psi(m+1) + \psi(m+\nu+1)]\left(\frac{x}{2}\right)^{2m+\nu}$$

which is known as the *modified Bessel function of the second kind and order* ν.

5. The Analytic Case

The differential equation

$$\mathbf{L}y = \frac{d^2y}{dx^2} + p_1(x)\frac{dy}{dx} + q_1(x)y = 0 \tag{1}$$

where $p_1(x)$ and $q_1(x)$ are analytic in a neighborhood of the origin is a special case of (2.2). One would suspect that in this case both solutions of (1) would be analytic. Let us show that the method of Frobenius will yield these solutions (that is, that the roots of the indicial equation are non-negative integers and the log term is absent.)

In the terminology of Section 2

$$x\,p_1(x) = p(x)$$

and

$$x^2\,q_1(x) = q(x).$$

Hence

$$\alpha_0 = 0, \qquad \beta_0 = 0, \qquad \beta_1 = 0$$

and

$$f_0(s) = s(s-1)$$
$$f_1(s) = s\alpha_1$$
$$f_r(s) = s\alpha_r + \beta_r, \qquad r \geqq 2.$$

The zeros of the indicial polynomial $f_0(s)$ are

$$s_1 = 1, \qquad s_2 = 0.$$

As usual, if we assume a solution of the form

$$y(x,s) = \sum_{n=0}^{\infty} a_n(s)\, x^{n+s}$$

where the $a_n(s)$ are determined by (2.8), then $y(x,1)$ is one solution:

$$y(x,1) = \sum_{n=0}^{\infty} a_n(1)\, x^{n+1}. \tag{2}$$

Since the roots of the indicial equation differ by an integer we must use (2.24). Thus we must compute A and the c_n. Now from (2.21)

$$A = \frac{F_1(0)}{1 \cdot G_0(0)} = f_1(0) = 0$$

since $G_0(\sigma) = 1$ [cf. (2.19)]. To compute the c_n we first construct the a_n. From (2.9) and (2.11)

$$a_n(\sigma) = \frac{a_0\, F_n(\sigma)}{f_0(\sigma+1) f_0(\sigma+2) \cdots f_0(\sigma+n)}. \tag{3}$$

But the first row in the determinantal expression for $F_n(\sigma)$ [cf. (2.10)] is

$$\sigma\,\alpha_1 \qquad (\sigma+1)\sigma \qquad 0 \qquad \cdots \qquad 0.$$

Thus since each term contains the factor σ,

$$F_n(\sigma) = \sigma\, P_n(\sigma)$$

where $P_n(\sigma)$ is a polynomial in σ. That is, $F_n(\sigma)$ *contains the factor* σ. Hence from (3)

$$a_n(\sigma) = \frac{a_0\, P_n(\sigma)}{(\sigma+1)^2(\sigma+2)^2 \cdots (\sigma+n-1)^2(\sigma+n)} \tag{4}$$

and

$$a_n(s_2) = a_n(0) = \frac{a_0\, P_n(0)}{n!(n-1)!}. \tag{5}$$

We recall that $b_n(\sigma) = \sigma\, a_n(\sigma)$ and

$$c_n(\sigma) = \frac{\partial}{\partial\sigma} b_n(\sigma) = \frac{\partial}{\partial\sigma} \sigma\, a_n(\sigma).$$

Thus

$$c_n(\sigma) = \sigma \frac{\partial}{\partial\sigma} a_n(\sigma) + a_n(\sigma).$$

Since $a_n(\sigma)$ is finite at $\sigma = 0$,

$$c_n(0) = a_n(0).$$

Comparing with (2.24), we see that

$$\bar{y}(x,0) = \sum_{n=0}^{\infty} a_n(0)\, x^n. \tag{6}$$

Hence (2) and (6) are two linearly independent solutions of (1).

REFERENCES

Bieberbach, L., *Theorie der Differentialgleichungen*, Dover Publications, New York, 1944.

Bôcher, M., *Leçons sur les méthodes de Sturm*, Gauthier-Villars et Cie., Paris, 1917.

Darboux, G., *Leçons sur la théorie générale des surfaces*, Gauthier-Villars et Fils, Paris, 1889, Vol. II.

Ince, E. L., *Ordinary differential equations*, Dover Publications, New York, 1944.

Kamke, E., *Differentialgleichungen reeller Funktionen*, Chelsea Publishing Company, New York, 1947.

Murray, F. J., and Miller, K. S., *Existence theorems for ordinary differential equations*, New York University Press, New York, 1954.

INDEX